THRIVING

Health is Your Greatest Wealth

THRIVING
Health is Your Greatest Wealth

CONTRIBUTORS

Anna Von Zinner

Don Tolman

Erika Cramer

Fred Liberatore

Fur Wale

Jayne Craig

Julide Turker

Marcus Pearce

Mark Collins

Monique Sarup

Myrna Manalili

Robert Hall

Tanya Leyson

First published in 2022 by Dean Publishing
PO Box 119
Mt. Macedon, Victoria, 3441
Australia
deanpublishing.com

Cataloguing-in-Publication Data
National Library of Australia
Title: Thriving: Health is Your Greatest Wealth
Edition: 1st edn
ISBN: 978-1-925452-51-8
Category: Health/Nutrition/Personal Development/Self-Help

This book is dedicated to all of the people in the world who see health as their greatest wealth, those who understand that health is about a holistic approach, and people who are looking for inspiration for their own health journey.

Know that there are so many approaches to health out there, and that health comes in many shapes and forms – you just need to make a shift, believe in yourself, take action and never give up!

YSHIFT? Because without our health, we struggle to live fulfilling, happy lives.

CONTENTS

We are sharing more in the INTERACTIVE book.

See exclusive downloads, videos, audios and photos.

DOWNLOAD it for free at deanpublishing.com/yshift/thriving

INTRODUCTION

Stories transform lives – I have seen it happen time and time again. Each and every inspirational story has the power to change lives, and they *do*. Maybe your story will have a profound impact on someone's health journey, or maybe someone else's story will truly impact how you approach your health.

Our authors all have one goal in common: to share forward their teachings, to help others with their health advice and experiences. They share one theme: that your health is your greatest wealth.

When someone has experienced similar circumstances to us, we can truly connect with and understand their story and think about its relevance in our own lives. Often, someone else who has 'been there and done that', who has gone through similar experiences and come out the other side, can be a beacon of hope. We can look at their health journey and story, and it can help us feel less alone and like we, too, can get through whatever we are experiencing. Again and again, these people who share forward their stories can inspire, empower and help others shift their lives. This is where I have discovered that the power of story – if shared forward – can change the world.

We are all unique, with our own story, life experiences, challenges and dreams. The world is full of ordinary people with extraordinary stories and abilities. These people may have been affected by tragedy, or challenged far beyond what we think we could endure. They are testament to the human spirit that resides in each and every one of us, keeping us going.

The authors in the YSHIFT series are all real, genuine people, telling you their story in their own words. These stories are told in an approachable, candid way. They're real and congruent. They're about triumphing over tragedy, building their health in their own way, and embracing their passion, purpose and life. These stories are about truly living life to the fullest.

In this book, you'll read many stories about health. We'll hear from men and women who are sharing their experiences in the hope that it will help someone. Their stories are about overcoming illness, gaining confidence and achieving a healthy mindset, finding healthy ways to approach ageing and work, nutrition, looking within to be your best, how you're showing up in life, the importance of community and relationships for health, fitness, alternative holistic solutions, and mental health and growth.

We'll look at holistic approaches and alternatives to Western medicine, because health is about more than just being free of disease or illness, it's about living in a state of vitality and optimal wellbeing physically, mentally and emotionally. There is a time and place for medical intervention, but at other times, you can take control of your health and wellbeing.

I began this series because I believe in the power of story – every person has something they can share with others. Whether it's about fitness, nutrition, mental health, or confidence, there is a jewel within everyone. The beauty of this series is that the openness of each author doesn't stop at the end of their chapter. The entire idea of the series is that you, the reader, can connect with any of these authors. You can contact them, learn more about them, find out more about their products or services, or simply drop them a line to thank them for sharing their story.

We also invite you to join the interactive YSHIFT Library, where we continue to share powerful, life-enriching stories on wealth, relationships, resilience, spirituality, beauty, business and more. This library will include additional videos, audio, images, helpful tips, contact information and other helpful and educational content.

So, join us in sharing forward these extraordinary stories: a shift for one – if shared – can equal a shift for many.

Susan Dean
Founder and CEO of YSHIFT
Your Share-It-Forward Teachings
www.yshift.global

THE
WHOLEFOOD
MEDICINE MAN

DON TOLMAN

DON TOLMAN

When it comes to taking care of your health, Don Tolman's – AKA 'The Wholefood Medicine Man's' – fundamental wisdom is that you seek the truth. Do your homework, and only then choose a path that seems logical, reasonable, and right for you.

Having been in the public arena for over 50 years, Don Tolman has been involved with doctors, medical groups, and scientific researchers – working with thousands of people who are seeking alternatives to the traditional healthcare system. A staunch believer in the power of clean air and water, sunshine, exercise, wholefoods, healthy relationships and a passion for life, Don asserts that it is up to the individual to take control and care of their own health, rather than rely on the institutionalised medical industry.

Don has travelled the globe as a public speaker, sharing his self care message to both live seminar audiences and through the international media. In the USA, Don has been a return guest on the Donahue Show, Entertainment Tonight and ABC Talk Radio. In Australia, he has featured on Mornings with Kerri-Anne, Today Tonight and countless talk-back radio shows.

Don now runs Tolman UniverCity – a unique service that educates clients on the principles of health, wellness, body systems and disease. Don also offers a range of supplementary products, such as CBD oils, toiletries, and cleansers to assist clients on their health journeys.

You can connect with Don at www.tolmanunivercity.com and www.dontolman.com.

As an international speaker, I have spent much of my career travelling to different cities every week. I *love* my topic. I share ideas on health, wholefoods, memory, and organic intelligence. These days, I work remotely. From my home in Mexico, I help people via online consultations and through Tolman UniverCity, a program that I have developed to teach the ins and outs of health and wellbeing to a worldwide audience.

To the person reading this chapter: I wish I could talk to you face to face. There is nothing more I enjoy than connecting with likeminded people on health and wellness, one on one. It is true that printed words are like dried flowers – the substance is there but the perfume gone. So, within these few pages, I hope to share my message with you, even if its sweet aroma cannot waft through your nostrils.

WHAT IS NUTRITION?

The impact that food has on our health is profound. It gives us energy, it sustains us, and it heals us. However, in our modern society, we have turned to pills, capsules and other drugs to carry out many of food's duties.

'Nutrition' is a two part word, with 'nut' being derived from the Latin 'nux' which means 'light', and 'rition' meaning 'process'. In other words, the true origins of the word nutrition, means 'process of light'.

So, by definition, something that is nutritious should have some form of electrical energy or life force. Logically speaking, this means it must be 'living'.

There are seven known ways of taking in light, and eating plants is one of them. Plants synthesise water and light to make and sustain themselves. When we chew the plants in our mouths, it is called making the *bolus*, a Latin word meaning 'round mass' or 'lump of earth'. 'Metabolise' comes from 'meta', meaning 'after change', and *bolus*, to 'throw a lump'. Some call this process digestion. This process is how wholefoods become recognisable by the cells or as light or photo-electrochemical messages. It is accomplished in the alimentary canal. This canal is a lined tube that runs like a river from the mouth to the anus and includes the pharynx, larynx, oesophagus, stomach and intestines.

The food is made into a *bolus* in the mouth, then sent to the stomach which turns it into *chyme* – stomach fluids and partially digested foods (let's call that 'lumpy juices'). It is then sent to the small intestine where it is turned from 'lumpy juice' into *chyle* – a smooth milky fluid. This process is performed by the lacteals who then move the 'milk' into the bloodstream through the thoracic duct so that cells everywhere can nurse or suckle upon the energetic messages of the 'milk's' composition in order to synthesise from the encoded liquid communications what each cell needs to know to keep and maintain life within itself.

Cells do not assimilate the milk. They read the photo-electrochemical messages. Then, like plants, they make what they need from water and light. When the messages in the milk are used up, the milk condenses back from a liquid to a solid state in the colon as water is reabsorbed into the body.

In short, the mouth takes the groceries in, and the rectum pushes the garbage out through the anus.

WHY WHOLEFOODS?

'To nourish, to sustain, and to enliven' is the gift of wholefoods – all we have to do is enjoy metabolising them. We might do well to ask, "How much life and light is in a dead calf's liver? The leg of a frozen chicken? A pill or a capsule?" Dry an apple, plant it, water it. The apple can propagate several trees that produce mountains of fruit. Plant a pill or capsule – will it grow? Will it even mould?

Eating wholefoods is the best way to pack your body full of nutrients. Wholefoods heal and clear your body of toxins, providing you with higher energy and a greater life. I have outlined some of the other ways in which wholefoods are beneficial to your health below.

1. **Wholefoods are the most nutrient dense**

   Nutrient density is a measure of the amount of nutrients a food contains in comparison to the number of calories. A food is more nutrient dense when the level of nutrients is high in relation to the number of calories the food contains. By eating wholefoods, you will get all of the nutrients you need – vitamins, minerals, phytonutrients, essential fatty acids, fibre – to ensure excellent health.

2. **The healthiest foods are wholefoods**

   Wholefoods are complete due to their rich, natural endowment of nutrients. They have not been highly processed, nor do they contain synthetic, artificial or irradiated ingredients.

   Whenever possible, healthy eating means purchasing 'earth friendly' grown foods – foods that not only promote your health, but also the health of our planet.

3. **Most of the healthiest foods are familiar foods**

   The healthiest foods are common 'everyday' foods. These include the fruits, vegetables, wholegrains, nuts and seeds, oils, herbs and spices that most people are accustomed to using.

4. **The healthiest foods are readily available**

   Although there are many foods that are exceptionally nutritious, many of them are not perennial or available across the world. The healthiest foods are therefore those that can be easily found at your local market, as they will not have been stored or transported for long periods of time to make it to your destination.

5. **The healthiest foods are affordable**

   Wholefoods that are affordable are best, as it generally means there is a surplus of in-season produce that is fresh and of high quality.

6. **The healthiest foods taste good**

   The healthiest foods are also some of the world's best tasting, as they are more fresh and flavoursome. Find and create recipes using wholefoods that do not overpower, but enhance, the unique flavour of each food.

   It appears that we are, by design, supposed to experience pleasure in all that we do. I have yet to hear of anyone swallowing a capsule and remarking, "Yum, that tasted and smelt good!" Where pills leave us feeling unsatisfied, wholefoods delight and pleasure us. This is a huge part of nutrition.

   Pleasure triggers the brain chemistry that prepares and activates the entire metabolic nutritional process for acceptance by the cells. The cells wait for delivery in great anticipation. You can feel their excitement. Just observe babies who are hungry and see their food coming.

7. **Plant wholefoods are always under attack**

   E Coli, Salmonella and other potentially deadly critters only come from animals with intestines. Yet, we are often fed the story that a vegetarian or vegan diet can not possibly offer all the benefits of an omnivorous one. This is simply not true.

FOOD IS MEDICINE

The natural world is crammed with produce that aids our physical health. These include:

- **Carrots**

A sliced carrot looks like the human eye – the pupil, iris, and radiating lines are all there. And yes, science now shows carrots greatly enhance blood flow to, and function of, the eyes.

- **Tomatoes**

A tomato has four chambers and is red, like the heart. All of the research shows that tomatoes are loaded with lycopene and are indeed pure heart and blood food.

- **Grapes**

Grapes hang in a cluster that has the shape of the heart. Each grape looks like a blood cell and all of the research today shows that grapes are also profound heart and blood vitalising food.

- **Kidney Beans**

Kidney beans heal and help maintain kidney function. And yes, they look exactly like the human kidneys.

- **Celery, Bok Choy, and Rhubarb**

These vegetables look just like bones and specifically target bone strength. Bones are made up of 23 percent sodium, as are these foods. If you don't have enough sodium in your diet, the body pulls it from the bones, making them weak. These foods replenish the skeletal needs of the body.

- **Avocadoes, Eggplant and Pears**

These vegetables target the health and function of the womb and cervix of the female – they look just like these organs. Today's research shows that when a woman eats one avocado a week, it balances hormones, sheds unwanted birth weight, and prevents cervical cancers. *How profound is this?* It takes exactly nine months to grow an avocado from blossom to ripened fruit.

There are over 14,000 photolytic chemical constituents of nutrition in each one of these foods – modern science has only studied and named about 141 of them.

• Figs
Figs are full of seeds and hang in pairs when they grow. Figs increase the mobility and numbers of sperm to overcome sterility.

• Sweet Potatoes
Sweet potatoes look like the pancreas and actually balance the glycaemic index of diabetics.

• Olives
Olives assist the health and function of the ovaries.

• Oranges and Grapefruits
Oranges and grapefruits, as well as other citrus fruits, look just like the mammary glands of the female and actually assist the health of the breasts and the movement of lymph in and out of the breasts.

• Onions
Onions look like the body's cells. Today's research shows that onions help clear waste materials from all of the body's cells. They even produce tears which wash the epithelial layers of the eyes. A working companion, garlic, also helps eliminate waste materials and dangerous free radicals from the body.

Specific foods will also target the brain and nervous system. Those foods are listed below:

• Almonds
Greek name is amygdala, a part of the brain
Almonds increase blood supply to the brain. Their nutrients target the activity of the brain, particularly relating to our emotions. Almonds are an ancient food that have been written about in historical texts, including the Bible. They were thought to have originated in regions in western Asia

and north Africa. The Romans referred to almonds as the 'Greek nut' in reference to the civilisation suggested to have first cultivated them.

• Apples

Apples protect and heal every bodily system, organ, and function. In other words, all of our cells love apples! But because apples are such commonly consumed fruits, we often overlook their amazing and unique health benefits.

Apples combine nutrients in a way that sets them apart from all other foods, even other fruits. This makes them a food of choice for achieving all health goals. When it comes to heart health, all of us need to keep blood circulating through our bodies (1,776 gallons are pumped by our hearts every day!). Apples contain a long list of phytonutrients (plant nutrients) that function as protectors/inhibitors (antioxidants) and support our heart health. To take full advantage of the nutrients in apples, it's important to include the skins.

I always recommend the purchase of organically grown apples. This minimises the apple skin's exposure to unwanted pesticide sprays and other potential contaminants.

Protectors/inhibitors aren't the only reason to include apples in a heart supportive diet. You will get about four grams of dietary fibre in a medium-sized apple. Included in this total amount is both insoluble fibre (cellulose) and soluble fibre (pectin). Pectins clear heavy toxic metals out of the brain.

• Blueberries

In human studies, researchers have found that blueberries help protect the brain from oxidative stress and reduce the effects of age related conditions such as Alzheimer's disease and dementia. Researchers found that diets rich in blueberries significantly improved both the learning capacity and motor skills of the ageing, making them mentally equivalent to much younger people.

Blueberries also act as an unusual type of probiotic by blocking attachment of bacteria that cause urinary tract infections. They contain chemicals that curb diarrhoea and are high in natural aspirin.

As I've mentioned before, every plant food helps the entire body. When the blueberry clears the urinary tract, the bowels and lung function improve. This benefits the brain greatly.

• **Broccoli**
Brain and full body support

Broccoli is a member of the cabbage family and is closely related to cauliflower. Its cultivation originated in Italy. *Broccolo*, its Italian name, means 'cabbage sprout'. Because of its different components, broccoli provides a range of tastes and textures, from soft and flowery (the floret) to fibrous and crunchy (the stem and stalk). Do not let the smell of the sulphur compounds that are released while cooking keep you away from this highly nutritious vegetable.

Like other cruciferous vegetables, broccoli contains the phytonutrients sulforaphane and the indoles, which have significant remissive cancer effects. Research on indole-3-carbinol shows this compound helps deactivate a potent estrogen metabolite (4-hydroxyestrone) that promotes tumour growth, especially in estrogen sensitive breast cells, while at the same time increasing the level of 2-hydroxyestrone, a form of estrogen that can be cancer protective. Indole-3-carbinol has been shown to suppress not only breast tumour cell growth, but also cancer cell metastasis (the movement of cancerous cells to other parts of the body). Scientists have found that sulforaphane boosts the body's detoxification enzymes, potentially by altering gene expression, thus helping to clear potentially carcinogenic substances more quickly.

When researchers at Johns Hopkins studied the effect of sulforaphane on tumour formation in lab animals, those animals given sulforaphane had fewer tumours, and the tumours they did develop grew more slowly and weighed less. Broccoli is in the same neighbourhood as apples in targeting first the brain and then the whole body.

• **Brussels Sprouts**
Brain, breast, and full body support. Offers cancer protection from special sulphur containing phytonutrients.

It is no surprise that Brussels sprouts look like perfect miniature versions of cabbage since they are closely related. Both vegetables belong to the *Brassica* family of vegetables.

Plant phytonutrients found in Brussels sprouts enhance the activity of the body's natural defence systems to protect against disease, including cancer. Scientists have found that sulforaphane, one of the powerful glucosinolate phytonutrients found in Brussels sprouts and other cruciferous vegetables, boosts the body's detoxification enzymes, potentially by altering gene expression. This helps clear potentially carcinogenic substances more quickly.

• Cabbage
Helps your brain get ahead by making it a clean machine!

Sturdy, abundant, and inexpensive, cabbage is a longstanding dietary staple throughout the world and is so widely cultivated and stores so well that it is available throughout the year. However, cabbage is at its best during the late autumn and winter months when it is in season. Cabbage belongs to the Cruciferae family of vegetables along with kale, broccoli, collards, and Brussels sprouts.

For about 20 years, we've known that many phytonutrients work as protectors/inhibitors to disarm free radicals before they can damage DNA, cell membranes and fat-containing molecules, such as bad cholesterol. Now, new research is revealing that phytonutrients in crucifers, such as cabbage, work at a much deeper level. These compounds signal our genes to increase production of enzymes involved in detoxification, the cleansing process through which our bodies eliminate harmful compounds. Recent studies show that those eating the most cruciferous vegetables have a much lower risk of brain, prostate, colorectal and lung cancer.

• Rockmelon (cantaloupe)
Brain and eye support. Vision food.

The cantaloupe derives its name from the Italian papal village of Cantalupo, where it was first cultivated around 1700 AD. It belongs to the same family as the cucumber, squash, pumpkin, and gourd, and like many of its relatives, grows on the ground on a trailing vine.

Cantaloupe is also referred to as a netted melon because it has a 'ribless' rind with a distinctive netted skin. Inside the melon is a hollow cavity that contains seeds encased in a web of netting. Many of the cantaloupes available today are hybrids of muskmelons and true cantaloupes and have qualities that reflect both.

Cantaloupe contains high levels of vitamins A and C, potassium, and is a good source of vitamin B6, dietary fibre, folate, and niacin (vitamin B3). The combination of all these B complex vitamins along with the fibre found in cantaloupe make it an exceptionally good fruit for supporting brain and body energy production through good carbohydrate metabolism and blood sugar stability. These B complex vitamins are required in our cells for processing carbohydrates (including sugars). The fibre within cantaloupe helps ensure that the fruit's sugars are delivered into the bloodstream gradually, keeping blood sugar on an even keel.

• **Cauliflower**
Brain power.
The cauliflower lacks the green chlorophyll found in other members of the cruciferous family of vegetables like broccoli, cabbage, and kale because the leaves of the plant shield the florets from the sun as they grow. Cauliflower has a compact head (called a 'curd') that is usually about six inches in diameter and is composed of undeveloped flower buds. The flowers are attached to a central stalk, which this looks like the brain and spinal cord. This wonderful food has all the same benefits of cabbage and broccoli, but focuses its powers on the 'white matter' of the brain and spine by cleansing them of toxins and waste materials. Then the brain can clear cancers and problems throughout the body, especially the prostate.

• **Ginger**
Cleans brain mass (amongst other things…).
The flesh of the ginger rhizome can be yellow, white, or red in colour, depending upon the variety. It is covered with a brownish skin that may either be thick or thin, depending upon whether the plant was harvested when it was mature or young. The ginger rhizome has a firm, yet striated texture and a taste that is aromatic, pungent, and hot.

Native to Southeast Asia – a region whose cuisines feature this wonderfully spicy herb – ginger has been renowned for millennia in many areas throughout the world. Ginger is mentioned in ancient Chinese, Indian and Middle Eastern writings, and has long been prized for its aromatic, culinary and medicinal properties. After the ancient Romans imported ginger from China almost 2000 years ago, its popularity in Europe remained centred in the Mediterranean region, until the Middle Ages when its use spread throughout other countries. Although it was a very expensive spice – owing to the fact that it had to be imported from Asia – ginger was still in great demand. In an attempt to make it more available, Spanish explorers introduced ginger to the West Indies, Mexico and South America, and in the 16th century, these areas began exporting the precious spice back to Europe.

Historically, ginger has a long tradition of being very effective in alleviating symptoms of gastrointestinal distress. In herbal medicine, ginger is regarded as an excellent carminative (a substance which promotes the elimination of intestinal gas) and intestinal spasmolytic (a substance which relaxes and soothes the intestinal tract). Modern research has revealed that ginger possesses numerous therapeutic properties including protector/ inhibitor effects, an ability to inhibit the formation of inflammatory compounds, and direct inflammatory healing effects.

Ginger also calms vomiting and has been shown to be very useful in reducing nausea and vomiting during pregnancy, even in its most severe form – hyperemesis gravidarum (a condition that usually requires hospitalisation). In a double-blind trial, ginger root brought about a significant reduction in both the severity of nausea and number of bouts of vomiting in 19 of 27 women in early pregnancy (less than 20 weeks). Unlike antiemetic drugs, which can cause severe birth defects, ginger is extremely safe and only a small amount is required to be eaten to be effective. A review of six double-blind, randomised controlled trials with a total of 675 participants, published in the April 2005 issue of the *Obstetrics and Gynaecology Journal,* has confirmed that ginger is effective in relieving the severity of nausea and vomiting during pregnancy. The review also confirmed the absence of any side effects or adverse effects on pregnancy outcomes.

• **Lettuce**
Lettuce keeps the heart young and the brain fun!
Most varieties of lettuce exude small amounts of a white, milky liquid when their leaves are broken. This 'milk' gives lettuce its slightly bitter flavour and its scientific name, *Lactuca sativa,* derived from the Latin word for 'milk'. Native to the eastern Mediterranean region and western Asia, lettuce has a long and distinguished history. With depictions appearing in ancient Egyptian tombs, the cultivation of lettuce is thought to date back to at least 4500 BC. The ancient Greeks and Romans held lettuce in high regard both as a food and for its therapeutic medicinal properties. Lettuce is an excellent source of vitamin A, folate, vitamin C, manganese, and chromium. In addition, romaine lettuce is a very good source of dietary

fibre, vitamin B1, vitamin B2 and the minerals potassium, molybdenum, iron, and phosphorus and about 9,000 other phytolith nutrients. Lettuce targets the brain by clearing blood plaque and increasing blood flow.

• Pine Nuts

Depending upon the species, a single serve of the lowly pine nut can provide you with up to 14 grams of protein per serving, with each nut being between ten to 34 percent protein. They're also an excellent source of fibre, vitamins E and K, and niacin. In terms of minerals, pine nuts are rich in magnesium and potassium which is important for maintaining a healthy heart and blood pressure.

It may surprise you to learn that pine nuts are actually a potent appetite suppressant. They're a good source of a polyunsaturated fat, known as pinolenic acid. When you eat a handful of pine nuts, the pinolenic acid stimulates the secretion of a hormone produced by the intestines, known as cholecystokinin (CCK). CCK sends the signal to your brain that you're full which turns off your appetite. It also helps to slow down the rate at which your stomach empties so you feel full and satisfied for longer.

• Walnuts
Food for better thought.

Walnuts have often been thought of as a 'brain food', not only because of their wrinkled brain-like appearance, but because of their high concentration of omega-3 fats. Your brain is more than 60 percent structural fat. For your brain cells to function properly, this structural fat needs to be primarily made up of omega-3 fats, usually found in nuts and seeds. This is because the membranes of all our cells, including our neurons, are primarily composed of fats. Cell membranes are the gatekeepers of the cell. Anything that wants to get in or out of a cell must pass through the cell's outer membrane. Omega-3 fats, which are especially fluid and flexible, make this process a whole lot easier, thus maximising the cell's ability to usher in nutrients while eliminating wastes.

Walnuts also have many potential health benefits ranging from cardiovascular protection, to the promotion of better cognitive function, to inflammatory removal benefits helpful in treating asthma, rheumatoid arthritis, and inflammatory skin diseases such as eczema and psoriasis. In addition, walnuts contain a protector/inhibitor compound called ellagic acid that supports the immune system and may also have several cancer remissive properties.

• **Watermelon**
Holds the same water content as the brain and delivers brain chemistry.
Watermelon targets brain function and, just like peanuts, has arginine, which prevents erectile dysfunction, lowers blood pressure, and improves insulin sensitivity. This sweet, crunchy, cooling fruit is exceptionally high in citrulline, an amino acid our bodies use to make another amino acid, arginine, which is used in the urea cycle to remove ammonia from the body. Arginine has been shown to improve insulin sensitivity in obese Type 2 diabetic patients with insulin resistance. When volunteers drank three glasses of watermelon juice each day for three weeks, blood levels of arginine (synthesised from citrulline provided by the watermelon) were 11 percent higher than in controls. Volunteers who drank six glasses of watermelon juice daily for three weeks had arginine levels 18 percent higher than controls.

If you have ever tasted a watermelon, it is probably no surprise to you how this juicy, refreshing fruit got its name. Watermelon has an extremely high water content, approximately 92 percent (the same as the brain), giving its flesh a crumbly and subtly crunchy texture and making it favourite thirst-quenching fruit.

THE WAR ON DISEASE

The human body is an infinitely complex marvel of fine design, superbly adapted to its functions. A host of specialised organs, bones, muscles, nerve fibres, blood vessels, and other anatomical features work together in harmony to maintain the network of interrelated body systems necessary to maintain life.

In fact, the human body is so complex that even today not all of its functions are completely understood. Certain cells are directed by genes to divide into organs with specialised functions. The senses of sight, smell, touch, taste, hearing, intuition, and imagination connect us to the outside world. The body is capable of detecting minute changes in the environment. It can adapt to different conditions and extremes of heat and cold. Quickly, it can prepare for fight or flight to protect itself from danger.

However, when the problem is within, as tiny as a bacterium or virus, the body has its own protective mechanism in the form of white blood cells and immune cells that neutralise the invader. Many ingested poisons are made harmless in the liver; waste products are efficiently excreted by the kidneys, alimentary canal, bladder, lungs, and skin.

Did you know?

• The human body can perform amazing acts of strength and grace. A highly trained athlete can push the body to the limit of its powers.

• A baby has close to 800 bones that fuse together over time. The skeletal system includes more than 200 bones and makes up about 18 percent of the body's weight by 22 years old. It provides us with a sturdy framework. Bone is strong, yet light and flexible.

• The muscular system consists of nearly 700 muscles and makes up about 40 percent of the body's weight. Muscles can contract which enables the body to move.

• The human eye, like many parts of the body, rapidly adjusts to changes in a darkened room. The pupil of the eye opens wide, so it lets in more light. If the lights are turned up, the pupil automatically shrinks within seconds.

• The heart is a powerful pump. It beats about 100,000 times each day as it sends blood throughout the body.

• The brain is one of the body's most complicated parts. The outer surface of the brain is made up of around 20 billion cells. It is interesting – there appears to be as many stars in our galaxy as there are neurons in our brain. It's almost as if we are a microcosm of the macrocosm.

• A microscopic view of the skin shows bacteria as tiny green balls. Countless bacteria live on the skin – billions and trillions. These bacteria are harmless and are meant to be there, unless they enter the body through a break in the skin which can lead to infection and inflammation.

• People sometimes call the human body a 'machine', the most wonderful one ever built. Of course, the human body is not a machine, but the comparison holds up in many ways. Like a machine, the body is comprised of many parts, and each part performs a special job. The parts all work together to make the body run smoothly. Also, like a machine, the body needs energy to work. In a machine such as an automobile, the energy comes from gasoline. In the body, the energy comes from air, water, sunshine, whole plant foods, movement, pleasure, and even passion.

• Although the human body can be compared to a machine, it is far more amazing than any mechanism ever built. It can do things that no machine can do. For example, the body can grow. The body starts out as one cell. That one cell, over a seven day period, divides into two. Seven days after that, it becomes four. Then, in periods of seven, it keeps doubling. From four to eight, from 16 to 32, from 64 to 128! After 40 weeks, there are close to ten thousand trillion cells that make up the body. In time, that very first, tiny cell was able to develop into a body consisting of trillions of cells.

• The human body can replace certain worn-out parts. Each day, several billion cells die and are replaced through cellular division. Thus, the body is always rebuilding itself. Every 35 to 45 days for instance, the human body replaces its outermost layer of the skin.

ANATOMY

Anatomy is the study of the biological structure of living things. The term comes from Greek words meaning 'to cut up', because knowledge of anatomy was first obtained through dissection. The bodies of human beings and animals are so complex that observers divided anatomy into many branches. Gross anatomy is the study of structure which can be seen with the unaided eye. Microscopic anatomy, or histology, is the study of tissues under a microscope. Comparative anatomy compares the structure of different animals. Embryology is the study of the development of plants and animals in their earliest stages.

Human anatomy includes the study of the structure of the skeleton, muscles, nerves, and the various organs of the human body. A knowledge of the structure of the body is essential for an understanding of its function, which is called physiology.

In ancient times, people believed that the dead body was a sacred thing, and cutting it up ranked as a serious crime – an offense to the entire cosmos. After 400 BC, the Greeks allowed occasional dissections. The physician Galen, in the AD 100s, described many anatomical structures, but he based his work mainly on dissections of animals and treatment of injured gladiators. After 1300 AD, dissection and anatomy became a recognised part of body learning in Western Europe. In 1543, Andreas Vesalius published his classic work on anatomy, which was based on human dissections. Since then, progress has been made possible through continued research and various discoveries.

PHYSIOLOGY

Physiology is the study of how living things function. Studies can range from the most basic unit of organisms, to complex organs and their systems, such as the brain and digestive system. In people for example, the digestion of food involves the action of hormones and other chemicals produced by the stomach, liver, and pancreas. Muscle contraction occurs through the action of chemical messengers produced by nerves that supply the muscle.

By learning how the body functions normally, we are better able to understand what happens when organs function abnormally. For example, the thyroid gland uses iodine, to make what today is called thyroxine, which is a hormone, or protein, that affects the entire body. If iodine is too low in the diet, the thyroid glands expand, forming a large mass called a goitre. This condition can be corrected by including iodine in the diet. The highest naturally occurring incidence of iodine is in mushrooms, the next being natural sea salt. Studies of the circulatory and nervous systems have helped people understand symptoms of heart disease, stroke, and even high blood pressure.

CARE FOR YOURSELF, BY YOURSELF

No long-living culture has ever taken a prescription or over-the-counter drugs. Not one of them has ever taken a pill, capsule, powder, or potion from the nutritional supplement industry. After 50 years of pharmaceuticals and 35 years of encapsulated herbs, powdered rocks, and miracle supplements, we are sicklier now than we ever have been.

Go out on a limb – don't leave it to others. Know your health, your body, and the benefits of the natural world that surrounds you.

Diet and bodywork is work for the 'yet unborn'. They will be born into better bodies, minds, and emotions, thanks to you caring for yourself.

"TAKE CARE OF YOUR MIND, YOUR BODY WILL THANK YOU. TAKE CARE OF YOUR BODY, YOUR MIND WILL THANK YOU."

– DEBBIE HAMPTON –

SWEAT SWEAR SMILE

FRED LIBERATORE

SHIFT

FRED LIBERATORE

With over four decades in the fitness industry, Fred Liberatore's knowledge and experience has created one passionate and sought-after Master Coach and Body Transformation Expert. From the moment he stepped into a gym as a young teenager, Fred was hooked on learning about health, nutrition and fitness. Fred's unique commitment to testing and measuring the countless techniques and fads that have come and gone over his fitness career, has empowered truly incredible results for himself and hundreds of his clients.

Fred knows what works and what doesn't and can tailor training programs to everyone's unique body type, needs and personal goals. Fred has the edge over 99% of personal trainers, coaches and health experts because he understands the physical aspect of training and nutrition in the finest detail. Fred combines this with the mental edge he has discovered after years of studying the world's top peak performance experts.

Fred's philosophy has always been to train hard, no excuses. His own peak fitness is a reflection of this, winning numerous bodybuilding titles which culminated in the coveted title of Mr Australia in the NABBA Masters in 2000. Fred went on to also win the NABBA Grand Master title in 2016.

Fred loves empowering people to achieve physical success no matter what their goal is. Supported by his devoted family and fitness team, Fred owns and operates RealFit gym in Melbourne, which takes coaching, training and nutrition to the next level. Fred's goal at RealFit is to create a holistic approach to health, nutrition and anti-ageing that inspires fulfilment in all aspects of life for his clients.

You can connect with Fred at www.leanmuscle.com and his Facebook group #leanmuscleenthusiasts.

A FITNESS LEGACY

If this chapter inspires just one person to shake themselves out of the physical slump they find themselves in and propels them in a more positive and healthy direction, then I have achieved my goal.

These pages are more than a chapter for me; they are a fitness legacy that I feel so excited to share following my four fulfilling decades living and breathing this great industry from end to end.

I hope these words will empower ordinary people to find the motivation and strength that I know is within them. The duality of my personal and fitness journeys over so many years has resulted in incredible transformations not only for myself, but for my clients as well. This evolution continues each day that I live and work in the business that I love: helping people find the best versions of their physical selves. This achievement has a wonderful impact on all aspects of their lives.

Imparting the lessons I've experienced over such a long time in this chapter is a small way to thank and give back to an industry that has been so inspirational and kind to me.

I am honoured to assist every individual who asks me to be a part of their fitness journey. As I watch them discover inner qualities they didn't know they possessed, I find myself learning something new from them, their challenges and how they dig deep to find the strength to overcome them. This experience with each person helps me to become a better version of myself too. What an amazing connection to look forward to each day!

I have been asked time and again to share my insights, my story, my experience – even my secrets – and through this writing process, I have been able to reflect on the long and windy road that led to my health and fitness dreams coming true. This has added to my own personal growth in a whole new way.

Every client I work with knows they will receive more than just personal training. It's not simply physical training, we also train the mind to go beyond its former limitations. I have high expectations for my clients to succeed and this spurs each person on to make a commitment with me and with themselves and they work even harder than they thought possible. They know if they want results – real, tangible, life-changing results – then I am the guy for them.

FIRST...BACK TO THE '80S

What a buzz it's been for me to look back on my upbringing and early life that paved the way for my fitness aspirations and launched me into such a fulfilling career. I had a fun, loving, working class upbringing around the inner northern suburbs of Melbourne. Life was discovered through experience and trial and error.

We relied on our imaginations for entertainment. When we weren't searching for spiders and other creepy crawlies in the dunny in our backyard, we'd take a few bats and balls to the small park near our house and spend hours replaying memorable sporting moments from our AFL or cricket heroes. There was no internet, no Google, and no mobile phones. Those were the days.

Growing up with older siblings and a very competitive twin made me obsessed with exercise, health and nutrition. My brother Tony (aka Libba) ventured on to become one of the most famous footballers in VFL/AFL history.

The importance of exercise was driven deeply into our DNA. I think Mum also found it a great way to ensure we didn't destroy our family home; after all, boys will be boys. Mum embraced the Aussie fixation on sport and we played AFL football in the winter months and cricket during summer. It was not an option to stay home. We needed to choose a sport and run with it.

We would have to work hard to save enough money for those special footballs and cricket bats we wanted. We mowed lawns and did odd jobs for our neighbours until finally our goal was reached and we'd buy the latest equipment to improve our sporting prowess. We'd play in the nearby park for endless hours with our friends and cousins until it got too dark to see what we were doing and we'd scurry home as fast as we could – sweaty smiles on our faces.

Each year, Tony and I would compete against each other in footy and often, either he or myself would win the Best and Fairest award for the season. I have to admit, footy gave me the foundation and groundwork to be the athlete I am today, especially playing at the senior level.

By employing a 'can do' attitude with grit and determination, both Tony and I tried out for the VFL Under-19 North Melbourne team. He was fast and very agile whereas I was slower and bulkier due to my thicker frame. My lower body muscle mass was starting to get in the way, especially during pre-season so speed and stamina was a challenge.

Around the age of 18, I found my passion for footy was dissolving and my drive to be more muscular was increasing. I realised football was not my calling or the path for me. After trying out with North Melbourne Under-19s the coach literally told me to get out after the first week. I was cut. I didn't blame him and we left on good terms. Such is the ruthlessness of elite sport.

Tony continued on and was very successful. As much as I enjoyed playing team sports, in all honesty, I was drawn to more solo sports where you can really test yourself individually. It was time to make some tough decisions with my footy career without procrastinating.

I wanted something different. I wanted to work my body from the inside-out. My frame started bulking up and at 19 years old, I already had well developed legs and was tipping the scales at 80+ kilograms and starting to see visible stretch marks, a result of my increasing workouts. As a teen I saw stretch marks as a positive indicator that my muscles were expanding.

I was really getting into this fitness thing. I added wrestling to my list of sports, which by the way, I still find one of the most challenging sports out there. I joined the gym and continued to physically push myself further and further. Part of this drive came from the fact that I wanted to have my own identity, separate to the growing fame of my twin.

People began referring to me as Tony's twin brother. I didn't have a name to them; I was simply 'his brother'. I know they never meant any harm; it's how people relate to one another or how people make connections. Looking back now, I understand why I worked so hard to find something that was just mine, to carve out my own, very different identity to his.

Now don't get me wrong, I have always been incredibly proud of Tony and I still am. Tony found his passion much earlier than I did. There was never a feeling of being left out in my family; we were always loved and treated equally. I personally felt though that I needed to find out who I was, without being defined by what my very successful twin was achieving.

My parents taught me from a very young age the value of hard work and that nothing comes to you without commitment. I landed my first part-time job at a supermarket stocking shelves. I would then take my pay and reinvest in myself by subscribing to medical journals to educate myself on the human body, all the while working out daily to obtain the body I was envisioning in my mind.

I was fascinated by real case studies of people who had transformed their bodies by sculpting them to be muscular and healthy. It was an ideal I aspired to. So I decided to reinvent myself as an individual, to re-engineer my identity and find my own path in life. The more I read and researched about the fitness potential of the human body, the more I found myself absorbed by it. Bodybuilding was drawing me in more and more every day, and I liked that I only had one person to compete against: me.

A MENTOR EMERGES

My older brother John witnessed my passion and appetite to learn more and decided to help me on my quest to be the athlete I was dreaming of.

The fitness industry in Australia began in the early '80s mainly marketed as aerobic exercise (who can forget the spandex wearing instructors on 'Aerobics OZ Style'?). While this may have been entertaining, there still wasn't much actual information out there about the science behind body and fitness. Quality gym equipment wasn't available either; it was clunky and poorly made at the best of times.

There was no easy way to improve muscle back then and we often had to improvise. One day John and I got creative with a few rusted, empty paint tins that were left over from when Dad painted the house. John saw their potential and made a barbell by filling them with cement and fixing an old rusty six-foot-long thick pipe between them.

I stumbled across a Spenby at my local Op shop. A Spenby was a chest expander with a quick-change snap link that would basically rip out any chest hair I had if I wasn't careful. I didn't care. I wanted it and I refused to wait a minute longer. That Spenby didn't help me make friends, but the allure of John's homemade barbell brought friends from every direction.

The repetition of using the barbell to press, pull and squeeze, worked every imaginable muscle in my body. I worked out tirelessly in the bungalow behind our Brunswick home with only the streetlight from the laneway allowing me to see. After the workout I'd scoff down a dozen bananas and guzzle a carton of full cream milk for nutrients.

My somewhat athletic frame was adding real muscle and John could see I was taking this exercise stuff seriously. I felt proud of my new body. I would brag about a new stretch mark on my upper chest area and show off my body whenever I could. John bought me a membership to our local gym called Fitzys. I was stoked and overwhelmed at what John had done for me. It felt like all my Christmases had come at once.

As soon as I stepped into that gym I was truly in muscle heaven. I saw bodybuilders with well-worn, ripped t-shirts, training their arses off, freely giving advice and spotting their fellow muscle builders with no mobile phone in sight. The good old days certainly were better without the devices. People would focus solely on what they were doing.

Not long after walking in the gym, I recognised a man from the magazines I subscribed to: a bodybuilder whom I worshipped. This guy literally had arms as big as my head. In my excitement, I ran over to him and blurted out, "Excuse me, how do I get big arms? What's a good exercise for a wide back? Can you show me how to do a skull crush?"

I was quickly told to back off and that if I wanted to see him, I would have to attend his seminar that evening. I was confused by his abrupt manner and the fact he was lying down with his feet elevated on a box reading a porno magazine!

At that moment, I realised I could become as built as he was with the right training and mindset. I could easily mirror his training style, not so much his reading style if you get my drift. My 'hero' did not end up meeting my expectations. He was egotistical and not a real advocate for health and wellbeing. He could have been using his time at the gym mentoring others. To me, this was a wasted opportunity. I believe every moment is a teachable moment and I knew straight away that I never wanted to have the same attitude as him. I wanted to be a mentor, a coach and someone to inspire others to be better. Just as my brothers John and Tony were my mentors, guiding and encouraging me to be the best I could be.

As my interest continued, I could already boast a very impressive collection of fitness magazines that I had invested in from the newsagency. I would be constantly reading and learning about bodybuilders like Lee Haney, Arnold Schwarzenegger and Lou Ferrigno. I would carry a pocketsized photo of my favourite bodybuilder in my wallet and had posters hanging behind my bedroom door.

Not only would I highlight the articles concerning my favourite athlete's diet and exercise programs, I would memorize them. That really heightened my interest in the science behind fat loss and the ultimate quest for lean muscle. I no longer went to the newsagency to read fitness magazines, instead I headed to the local library to delve deeper, sitting there for hours sifting through books on anatomy, learning how muscles worked and why.

I read research papers involving anything from the mindset behind weight loss and nutrition to exercise, fat loss and case studies around this. It would take me about a day to read through each article because I had to stop and check almost every word in the medical dictionary.

I had reached this point because I was over the smoke and mirror stuff you see in magazines promoting a miracle weight loss pill and potion. After years of reading about the 'latest and greatest' diet methods in magazines, I didn't know who or what to believe anymore. I found each magazine's newest diet method contradicted the diet method published in the previous month's edition. It was purely speculation; very few methods were based on science, while others were complete gibberish, defying the fundamental laws of thermodynamics and science.

When it came to losing weight and packing on lean muscle, every 'nutrition guru' and weight-loss personality had their own theory on what did and didn't work. Consumed by the hype, it was easy to ignore my previous doubts and think their absurd diet theory sounded logical (even though there was no scientific evidence to support the theories).

I noticed if an idea is published, and enough people accept it, it's perceived as true regardless if it's accurate or not. I saw how magazines would recycle unproven diet programs and confuse the reader to drive up sales each month – it helped pioneer the instant gratification generation.

So that's how I became resolved to 'test and measure' everything and see what did and didn't work. This has become my personal fitness philosophy. Through so many years of working with individuals of differing body types, different lifestyles, tastes and preferences, by testing and measuring various methods, I have developed a program to specifically focus on different areas of the body, and in conjunction with the best eating regime, my clients (and myself) are able to obtain the desired results in a realistic, sustainable timeframe.

Not long after this, around 1985, I started working at the council run gym at Broadmeadows Leisure Centre. When I wasn't working, I would wrestle. My obsession with fitness was at its peak and people were starting to notice.

My three goals when studying exercise, nutrition and mindset were to:

1. Learn everything I possibly could about nutrition and metabolism and its effects on the body.

2. Research those at the top of their game, break their model down and make it better.

3. Graduate with high marks as a gym instructor and massage therapist.

My obsession to learn about the human body led me to undergo a certificate in massage. Once qualified I offered sports massage from my parents' home to my fitness training partners who always complained about feeling sore. From massage I then studied and qualified as a Personal Trainer. Back when I graduated, personal training wasn't as big as it is now. You couldn't make a full time income out of it, so it began as a part-time gig for me.

THE FITNESS INDUSTRY DOES NOT ALWAYS GET IT RIGHT

I understand that fitness companies want to advertise their businesses. But often their strategy involves propagating a feeling of guilt and physical inadequacy in society. Statements like:

Get your beach body now!   *Get a sixpack in 14 days!*

Fit into your bathing suit in ten days!   *Overindulged? Take this product!*

These campaigns all imply you don't fit the idealised body. They also imply their superior product offers a magical 'quick fix' solution to your problem. Their focus is always on the extreme examples that are usually unattainable and target the masses, rather than focusing on the individual and creating sensible goals that apply to the person's unique situation.

Only the unscrupulous organisations hook clients in with enforced 12-month lock in contracts. Their business model is built on non-attendees and they will do anything to get them to sign on the dotted line. How does that make you feel? Like a faceless number? It's aggravating, isn't it?

On top of this, their websites show perfectly sculpted bodies. They propagate the message that looking good is the most important thing in life. The images that make up their publicity campaigns are smoke and mirrors, and represent a very small percentage of people who often make a living from their looks.

Those images are not realistic for most people. Even those few who do dedicate a lot of time to attend the gym, are still left feeling miserable and ignored when their gym does nothing to help them achieve their goals.

These companies do not cater for the real person balancing busy schedules trying to find time and genuine help for their own health. There are a range of 'normal' people that need slow, steady, solid and sustainable progress for their health. Loads of different body shapes fit into the 'normal' category and 'normal' is completely underrated in my experience.

In more recent times, I have seen positive shifts in the industry where workouts are becoming more functional. This means that even though some of these workouts seem repetitive and boring, their focus is on strengthening core muscles and the body as a whole. I also love that many places are now showing the practical value of transforming one's health through games, and I believe this should be the role of the fitness industry.

It sounds simple, but the joys of running, jumping and moving you felt as a child, can be found again by freeing up and strengthening those muscles. Fitness is fun so let's bring back playtime! I encourage you to take everything you read or hear with a grain of salt and I invite you to test and measure to find out if it's true for you.

MY LIGHT BULB MOMENT

The world changed on September 11, 2001 when America's Twin Towers were attacked. The events of that day also triggered an epiphany for me to seize the day.

At the time, I was working in international freight forwarding. It was a good job, I travelled the world and the pay was good, but I knew it was not my true calling. As many do, I worked in order to pay bills and put food on the table. I was weight training in my spare time; fitness was still very important to me.

When the Towers were hit, my twin brother Tony was in New York on a football trip. He was also with Australian tennis champion Lleyton Hewitt celebrating his US Open victory against Pete Sampras. I didn't know it at the time, but Tony had left the Tower only 30 minutes before the attack and so thankfully he escaped before the devastation took place.

However, the waiting to find out if Tony was okay and not knowing what was happening struck me as a huge awakening. Everything became very clear suddenly, like a light bulb had finally shone the spotlight on my deepest passion.

At that moment, I knew I could not waste any more time doing something I didn't love. I walked straight into my boss's office and said, "Mike, I'm not living my best life. I've got to go," and I walked out, never looking back. I had the will to succeed and the passion for personal training so I chose to pursue my dream. It hasn't always been easy, but it has always been worth it.

I obtained a job in a gym and worked myself up the chain, making some fantastic connections. I would write up programs, put weights away, open up in the early hours of the morning and lock up late at night. I loved being involved and having great conversations with people about their health goals.

Throughout my four decades in fitness, I have worked in all facets of the industry. From amateur enthusiast, massage therapist, personal trainer for small and national gyms, competing and winning competitions, working with an Australian supplement company in brand development and running their challenges and also being known as Australia's 'Master Coach', I have done it all. As I began to win competitions, I had professional photos taken as a way to mark and remember my accomplishments.

People would often look at me and say, "Wow Fred, I want your legs," or "How do you do it?" I developed such a depth of knowledge and breadth of experience that people were always coming up asking me for help. I would happily share any advice. I would write out a program for them if they asked, compile a list of what I was eating, or give them tips on getting bigger legs.

My massage, anatomy and physiology background enabled me to give them information from a wider, more rounded perspective. Often it wasn't just one thing that would help them move closer to their goal. It was about lifestyle changes too.

When I was training and saw someone doing an exercise wrong, it was really concerning because I knew that incorrect technique could potentially be harmful. So I'd walk over and introduce myself and say, "Hey buddy, it looks like you're doing that exercise wrong and you could get hurt. Can I show you the right way to do it?" They were always happy to hear some advice and talk about their own journey.

MY FITNESS PHILOSOPHY

My philosophy has always been to show up and be present in every moment. I believe you must train smart, not just hard.

My personal formula is: Sweat – Swear – Smile.

I know I've had a great session if I've done all three of these. I don't take excuses. I think everyone needs to find something they love, stick to it and give it a real go, not just for a week but at least for a few months. You want to be able to build momentum and momentum tends to develop with training and commitment over time.

The beauty of sticking to something for a while is that you can always trump your last session. You can always reach for a new height or goal to outdo yourself. The only person you can truly compete against is yourself.

Every time I train, I grade myself and the session out of ten. I ask my clients to do the same. Think about how you are feeling at the beginning and throughout the session, and what could have been done better. Neither my clients nor I have ever been a ten. We usually hover around the six to eight mark.

What I have experienced and witnessed is when you are consistent, your body and mind adapt and improve. My advice to you is to be present in the moment, have minimal distractions and be consistent. You may like to sit down with your diary and find some time you can dedicate to training and then lock it in!

I cannot emphasise enough that you really need to embrace nutrition, mindset and training when going down the fitness rabbit hole!

Let's look at my philosophy in more detail for a moment.

Sweat

Sweat is the cooling mechanism for the body and proof you've pushed yourself in the workout. Much information can be researched that explains the significance of sweating. Sweating is a contributing factor to controlling body temperature, making sure that you do not overheat. The human mechanism is so intelligent, and innately understands what to do for its optimal function.

Additionally, sweating assists in dampening or moistening the palms, which helps with gripping. There are cases where some people may experience excessive sweating, which is known as hyperhidrosis. This condition has no known cause, but it can be managed by reducing excess body fat and getting checked by your healthcare professional to make sure your hormones are in balance. Most people have normal sweating patterns in their lives caused by heat, working out and fever, among other things.

Lack of sweat is an indication you are dehydrated. Hydrate throughout the day and before you commence your workout. One of the ways we can see how effectively we have worked out, is by the amount we have sweated. If you are working out fully hydrated and find you are not sweating (or sweating sufficiently), then you are not working out hard enough!

You must raise your heart rate enough to bring on a sweat and that is when you know you are working out to your personal limit, which can always be outdone in your next workout. Once the same routine no longer breaks you out in a sweat, it's time to up your game.

A lot gets said about the amount of sweat people produce. Some men think they are fitter than their female partners because they sweat more. But there is a simple explanation for this: while females may have more glands, male sweat glands produce more sweat.

	PSYCHOLOGICALLY	PHYSICALLY	EMOTIONALLY
SWEAT	• Allows us to see the work is paying off making us feel good	• Clears your body of heavy metals and chemicals • Bacteria cleansing • Boosts immunity • Cools body down and regulates your body temperature • Fights disease when feeling unwell	• Gives us a sense of accomplishment • Improves mood and sleep
SWEAR	• Swearing enables us to go that bit extra	• Activates the amygdala resulting in more power • Elevates endorphins and serotonin levels • Increases circulation • Lowers pain levels	• Overall sense of happiness and release, calmness and wellbeing
SMILE	• Feel good factor • Puts you in the moment and you connect with yourself • Induces creativity (i.e. problem solving)	• Relaxes body and can lower heart rate and blood pressure • Endorphins act as a natural pain reliever • Boosts serotonin levels	• Uplifts mood • Boosts confidence and you smile more

Researchers found that females sweat less than males but still are able to maintain a normal body temperature. This is because females are more efficient sweaters than males. And why is this? Because female bodies evaporate sweat on their skin more efficiently, which cools down the body without a lot of perspiration.[1]

Are you ready to sweat?

Getting your heart rate up is a great way to get sweating.

Swear

I'm convinced that swearing during exercise improves performance and helps you deal with the f#&king pain. Dr Richard Stephen at Keele University, UK, tested the effects of swearing on anaerobic power.

The researchers organised two experiments where 29 participants firstly underwent a test of anaerobic power on an exercise bike for a short, intense period of time without swearing, and then repeated this activity while being allowed to swear. Another test saw 52 participants complete an isometric handgrip test again with no swearing and then with swearing. In both cases, participants produced more power and strength when they swore![2]

It's about channelling that energy into something positive. Swearing is a great strategy if used in the right way. Be careful though, nobody likes a potty mouth!

Smile

When we smile, we trick the brain that we're happy, triggering the release of the hormone cortisol as well as endorphins such as dopamine and serotonin that instantly lift your mood. When it comes to loading the squat rack, I smile and soldier on. It has worked for me so far as I'm squatting more than I ever have before.

In fact, smiling isn't just for weight workouts. Research from the Psychology of Sports and Exercise shows that smiling makes running easier and helps reduce muscle tension and distracts runners from uncomfortable body sensations.[3]

Using this three point system of **Sweat – Swear – Smile** will propel you to greater heights and I dare you to give it a go! I have created a quick reference guide that you can refer back to, to remind yourself of my personal philosophy. Feel free to add to it as you please and as you progress.

MINDSET IS EVERYTHING

I have three pillars of philosophy behind a successful fitness journey: training, mindset and nutrition. Each part is as important as the other but I believe the most important place to begin is with mindset. They say winning isn't everything but I say wanting to *is*.

Your attitude going into any challenge often determines your outcome. But, have you ever wondered where your attitude comes from? Growing up with a twin equally as competitive as I was played a big part in creating my never-give-up attitude.

Tony and I were always competing against each other, pushing ourselves and doing whatever it took to win. Sometimes we won; sometimes we lost. I recall one tough game of footy when we were young, Tony had been pretty confident he would take out Best On Ground, but that day I took the title. Tony elbowed me in the ribs all the way home in the back seat of dad's Volkswagen. I took the pain and rubbed it in even more. This was our constant competitiveness and today, we laugh and joke about it.

Imagining that moment of winning was a huge force behind our persistence and determination to keep going even after getting beaten. Eventually this would pay off in our individual achievements, we just had to hang in there. Tony's tenacity was unbelievable, it's what enabled him to launch fearlessly into a pack of much larger footy players and he'd be the one to emerge from between them all with the ball in his hands.

Back then I didn't understand 'how' I reached my goal; I just kept envisioning the result I wanted in my mind. I constantly remind my clients (and myself) that visualisation is the way to plant ideas and goals into your subconscious mind and a healthy way to create your own, personal vision statement. It's a matter of simply closing your eyes, using your imagination, and mentally creating the pictures in your mind, like running a movie of your desired results on repeat. This will then become the reality in your subconscious and replaying it with emotion will help you to change old habits and increase performance.

This is not a new technique and has been around for centuries. There are so many ways to use visualisation. It has been used in the field of sports psychology and personal development to increase stamina, reach personal and professional goals, and exceed any limits the athlete may have had before.

'Goal visualisation' is common with athletes across the globe and simply means that in their minds' eye they can already see themselves having achieved their goal, whether it be the desired body they are aiming for, the ideal lifting weight, or competing and winning in their chosen field.

A special teacher and friend once told me:

> *"Fred, the use of mental imagery is one of the strongest and most effective strategies for making something happen for you."*
> Dr Wayne Dyer

I have never forgotten that advice. My wish to meet Dr Wayne Dyer came true after reading many of his books (my favourite being *The Power of Intention*). I listened with great interest and intent when he presented a series of seminars in Sydney in 2001. Wayne's talks on stage about how your thoughts are your currency really ignited the possibility in me that I could create the life I imagined and not give in to the opinions of others. I could feel my worth, which focused my attention on my dreams in a positive way.

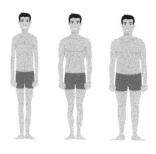

BODY TYPES

Let's get down to details to understand the factors that can affect your results even before you begin. For any training and nutrition program, it's a good idea to know your somatotype – your natural shape and size. There are three body types you are predisposed to fall under:

- Endomorph
- Mesomorph
- Ectomorph

Even within these categories, you can be a combination of two rather than a single type. Your genes, ethnicity, diet and exercise can influence your body type. Working with your body type (rather than against it) helps you create the healthiest, happiest and fittest you, naturally.

Ectomorph

Ectomorphs are lean with long, thin legs and arms, narrow chest and shoulders. Their fast metabolism makes it hard to gain weight and build muscle.

Even if an ectomorph manages to put on weight, they may look slimmer than they are, however they can become remarkably strong and as fit and healthy as someone who looks larger and more muscular. If this is your body physique and you wish to gain weight and muscles, you'll need to eat like you've never eaten before.

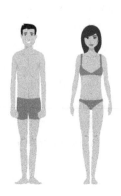

Suggested training techniques for ectomorphs: Most ectomorphs' goals are to build lean muscle and put on weight. Ectomorphs tend to eat copious amounts of food but never seem to gain any muscle mass. The type of training I recommend is to begin with very low impact and foundation movements, such as deadlifts, bench squats and military presses.

I suggest a repetition range of 4 to 12, with 4 sets and rest periods in between. Sets should be approximately 60 to 90 seconds and food intake should consist of whole foods and good fats. This will enable ectomorphs to get good results over time. The important thing is steady progress and that weight training does not sacrifice form.

Mesomorph

A mesomorph is naturally strong – strong arms and legs, a narrow waist, very little body fat, storing fat evenly across their body, and gains muscle easily.

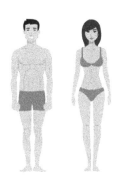

Suggested training techniques for mesomorphs:
A mesomorph body type, in my opinion, is the luckiest of the three. They can mix and match their workouts to suit their personal goals. The majority of this body type I have trained have aimed to lose up to about 7 kilos, so I mix it up between high and low volume exercises to see how they personally respond to the workout. Walking and sprinting works, the repetition range should be around 8 to 15 repetitions, 3 sets and rest periods of around 30 seconds.

Mesomorphs can generally consume more protein but they also need to adhere to proper nutritional principles.

Endomorph

The endomorphs have a wider build with a thick ribcage, wide hips, thicker joints and shorter limbs. While they are softer, rounder, curvier, stockier than other physiques, they may have more muscle than either of the other body types. They easily gain fat when adding muscle due to a slower metabolism.

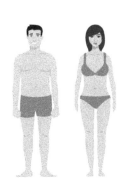

Suggested training techniques for endomorphs:
Endomorphs need to be pushed, and pushed hard (controlled of course). They should be doing high repetition ranges from 8 to 20 reps with reduced rest periods. I would avoid any high impact work initially as this can create injuries. Most endomorphs can have lower limb and knee issues such as shin splints due to the weight they are carrying. They must reduce their

calorie intake and put in the extra work in everything they do from nutrition to training to mindset.

The in-betweeners

In-betweeners are a combination of body types i.e. ectomorph/mesomorph or mesomorph/endomorph. In order to optimise your goal, it's important to know which one you are, and train and eat accordingly.

Understanding body type is a big part of the initial process when you get started on the Lean Muscle program.

STAY COMMITTED TO YOUR GOALS

From what I have seen over the years, when people do not quickly see the results they want, they get frustrated and lose sight of the end game. Ditch the instant gratification because results simply do not happen overnight.

Never quit or give up on YOU, and that will give you the strength to play the long game. You can change your goals, but remain dedicated to you. Taking action day after day builds the foundation brick by brick and prevents you from sliding backwards and undoing your hard work. Know you will only see small changes to begin with, but use a tape measure and the fit of your clothes as your guide.

The purpose of this chapter is to also teach you life-long principles. If you are serious about making fitness a regular part of your life, you need to reinforce these foundations by replacing habits that don't support your dreams with ones that do, such as a healthy lifestyle change.

If you want to develop strength and get a lean muscular body, it takes hours in the gym – not just a few here and there, but hours on a consistent basis. You need to pursue your goal by getting into the gym day in and day out. Just like you make it a habit to brush your teeth or watch television before bed, incorporate the habit of getting to the gym.

Working out does not require as much effort as you think. The key is to really make time for what is important in your life. Not only will training change your physiological appearance, but it will also provide you with the mental tools necessary to succeed in anything you do (i.e. finances, business, and education).

CONFIDENCE FEELS LIKE SH*T

ERIKA CRAMER

Y SHIFT

ERIKA CRAMER

Known as the Cardi B of the personal development world, Erika Cramer (aka The Queen of Confidence) is a full-flavored, spicy inspirational speaker and mentor to thousands of women across the globe.

Today, she connects with an engaged global community (The Sistahood) and shares with tens of thousands of women daily to help empower, encourage and inspire them to step into their confidence.

But it hasn't always been this way. Having survived many traumatic experiences in her youth, Erika spent a number of years searching for love, peace and validation in all the wrong places. She has survived childhood sexual abuse, being brought up in and out of the foster care system, life-altering car accidents and a whole lot of grief and loss.

In the last decade or so, Erika has been able to turn her life around from one of hopelessness and pain to one of passion, growth and success, after going on her own powerful journey of personal healing.

An international confidence coach, Erika also hosts a five-star rated podcast, *The Confidence Chronicles*, which is in the top ten of the Australian Apple charts for Mental Health, with 1.2 million downloads (and counting), and listeners in 79 countries.

She has created a six-figure global business from absolutely nothing, by mentoring and helping those who have suffered similar life experiences to her own.

Originally from the US, Erika was born in the small town of Framingham, Massachusetts. She has lived all over the US (Orlando, Miami, Boston and LA) due to being in the US Army for a decade, before moving to Sydney. Since 2011, Erika has called Melbourne home. She lives near the beach with her husband Hamish and their two sons, Raven and Navah.

Erika's story is one of triumph over adversity. She is full of light, laughter and of course, confidence. Erika is a beaming and beautiful example of how you can heal your personal story to transform trauma into triumph.

You can connect with Erika at www.thequeenofconfidence.com and on Instagram at @thequeenofconfidence.

HARNESS YOUR INNER HEALTH TO AMPLIFY YOUR LIFE

There's a truth I always start with, and it is: *confidence feels like shit.*

Here's the thing. It's such hard work to become confident, and the journey you've gotta go on to get there is an absolute rite of passage that knows no boundaries when it comes to feeling: embarrassment, shame, discomfort, fear and self-doubt.

It sucks, homegirl. But here's the flip side.

When you create your confidence – and I mean, true confidence – you enter a space where you retain a hundred percent of the power to choose how you feel, what you believe and how you want to experience your life. Being confident allows you to transcend all sorts of bullshit that holds you back, because it puts you in a place where you learn how to truly let go of what others think, say and believe about you.

The opinions and actions of all of these people who you currently allow to have 'real estate in your mind' will cease to exist, in terms of how much power, focus and energy you give them.

You may be thinking: WTF Erika?! How is this even possible? I've lived my whole life worrying about what 'they' will think of me.

The reason you won't care boils down to one simple fact: they'll get very little (if any) of your attention. Why? Because you'll have that deep, all-encompassing knowing and understanding that whatever they're doing or saying, or however they're acting, it's all about THEM and the demons they're battling, and it's got nothing to do with YOU.

NOTHING. (Feels freeing *AF* doesn't it?)

When you gain true confidence, you gain the freedom to truly live your life without limitations or constant negativity holding you back, because you become allergic to other peoples' opinions or projections.

Sounds amazing, right? It is! It's a pretty fucking incredible way to live. It's life-changing, in fact. And I know this – because this is how I now live my life.

I used to be a total wreck. I've been to hell and back in a hundred different ways for a hundred different reasons, and because of that I know what it's like to live in that space of *lack*. Of need. Of craving *validation, love* and *attention.* Of never, ever thinking I'll be 'enough' and of looking for love in all the wrong places (over and over and OVER again) in order to fill my cup and make me feel worthy or 'good enough'.

I've lived with confidence and without it, and let me say this: the path of confidence has the power to change your life in ways you never even imagined.

So, if that's the case, then what do I actually mean when I say that confidence feels like shit? It's an ethos. A way of life. And even more than that, it's an invitation for YOU (and women everywhere) to stop accepting less, while also being prepared to put in the hard yards it will take to get the life that you really want.

So instead of being cute, fluffy, and motivational – I am here to tell you straight up, early on that: **there are no shortcuts when it comes to gaining real confidence**.

There is no final destination or place to 'get to' where you can tick it off as done! Sorry sister, there's no sale on 'confidence'. It's not something you can order on Amazon.com, add five to your cart, choose overnight delivery and then, tada! *Instant confidence*

Like everything worth having in this life, you gotta do the work. And you have to be willing to fight for it – because, let me tell you, it's a freakin' fight to do this work!

How do I know? Because I have fought tooth and nail to find myself, to free myself and to build confidence in life. I have spent ten years and literally tens of thousands of dollars doing this work on myself. And let me tell you – it was a fucking shit-show. It took me time, money, effort and a new way of thinking to find my confident self.

THE MESSY ROAD TO CONFIDENCE

I'm from a broken, fatherless home; I've experienced sexual, verbal and physical abuse; I've lived in massive scarcity; I've been in and out of foster care my entire childhood; and I have survived more trauma and grief by the age of 25 than I'd ever imagined.

I want you to understand that every little moment and interaction has created who you are today. I want to tell you a bit of my story because I want you to know that **I get it**.

I get what it's like to doubt yourself and feel like you're not good enough.

I get what it's like to feel like no matter what you do, you'll never be enough.

I get what it's like to experience loss and feel completely alone.

I get what it's like to suffer with shame, guilt, abandonment, loneliness, anxiety and fear.

I get it.

When women see me on social media or come to one of my live events they usually think, "Oh, it's easy for you Erika, 'The Queen of Confidence' – it must be nice to be so positive and confident all the time." But that's actually not the case.

It wasn't (and it still isn't) 'easy' for me. It has actually been the hardest thing I've ever had to work on. I had to become greater than my environment and I had to transform every adversity I was faced with.

I had to learn how to shift my perspective on the shitty cards that life had dealt me. I had to change my perspective on how I saw my life and what I chose to focus on.

This is a choice we all have.

And the reason why I need to share my story with you is because, if I am honest – I really shouldn't be where I am right now. I technically 'shouldn't be' living the incredibly amazing life I am currently living.

But I didn't allow my fucked-up past to create a shitty future. My past doesn't get to define who I become.

And that's why I want to tell you about it.

What I'm about to share is really important. Not just because I want you to know my story, but because I need you to understand that when I tell you to "reclaim your confidence," to "stop letting your past determine your future" and to "take responsibility for healing your shit" – all of this comes from my own experience doing so. I walked the talk sister.

So as nice as it may sound to call myself the Queen of Confidence, don't get it twisted. There were a lot of dark times where I didn't know how the hell I would get myself out.

* * *

I was born and raised in a little city located 20 minutes outside of Boston, Massachusetts. My mum became a single mother when my dad left us, when I was two years old. Having been diagnosed bipolar, my mother suffered with manic episodes where she would stop her medication and get really, really sick.

During her manic periods, she would become physically and verbally abusive. Throughout my childhood and teen years, my mum was in and out of mental hospitals and I was in and out of the foster care system, living with different foster families.

And just in case you're wondering, my mother and I have an incredible relationship now. She is my hero – I mean, to raise a child on your own, living on food stamps, while battling with a mental illness…I can't even imagine. She suffered so much yet she NEVER gave up on me and she never stopped fighting to get me back.

Being in the foster care system was tough. As you may know, these systems in most countries need work. Although I loved living with other kids and changing schools and being in large groups, this is where my sexual abuse began. This is where I lost a lot of my innocence.

This back and forth, unstable upbringing led me to growing up as a kid who had anger issues. I tried to protect myself with anger and violence and being the 'tough girl'. But the reality was, I was sad, lonely and I felt like I wasn't good enough, smart enough or worthy of anyone's love.

My senior year in high school, I was off to bootcamp. I ended up being in the US Army for ten years (eight years' active duty, my last two years inactive) and moved across the country, marrying my high school sweetheart Jeo in secret as he went off to fight the war in Iraq (he too had joined the military in high school).

The year he got back from war, I decided I would put my dreams and desires on hold so we could chase his goals. After all, he went from high school to the Marines and hadn't really done anything else in his life. I suggested we move from California to Florida. I was 21 years old when we moved to Florida. And this is where my first major 'holy fuck' moment began.

When I was 23 years old, I woke up in the emergency room of the Orlando Regional Medical Center. There was a group of medical professionals hovering around me and someone was cutting my jeans off my legs.

In the background, I could hear my husband Jeovanni screaming and yelling. I had barely made it out alive from what was the most horrific drinking and driving car accident I had ever known of.

A few seconds passed, and I blacked out again. Jeo went into a coma for 12 hours after that, as he had severe head trauma.

The next time I woke up, I could see someone standing in the corner of the room. It was Virma Lopez, my Army supervisor.

The doctor was there and proceeded to tell me that I had fractured my back in two places and that the bone was damaged so badly, they needed to fuse it with titanium. My left ankle needed hardware to repair it as well.

"You're very lucky," he told me. "If you had been in any other position when you crashed, you could have been paralysed permanently."

"Accident? What accident?! Surgery, what are you talking about? What happened to me?"

I was in total shock, as I still had no idea why I was in hospital. At that moment, my memories started flooding back in snippets and bursts. *Oh, fuck.*

Jeo had been driving. Earlier that night, we'd been invited to a nightclub in downtown Orlando with some friends who had a VIP booth.

At the end of our 'fun' night, we got into the car to drive home. Now, I don't know how or why we made the decision on this night to get behind the wheel of the car (or how the hell the bar staff even let us leave the venue, as drunk as we were) but I do remember that when Jeo sat in the driver's seat and his friend got in the front passenger seat, I demanded in my drunkenness that they both put their seat belts on. But I never put a seat belt on myself.

You can imagine what happened next.

I woke up seconds before we crashed and well, it was too late. As our car was headed straight into a ditch, my vision went black.

We smashed into a ditch, which turned the car so we were facing backwards. We hit a van that was parked in the lot of a convenience store, and the van pushed us into a tree, which then smashed us against the convenience store brick wall.

I was later told that the Jaws of Life came to break the car open so they could get Jeo out and they took us via helicopter to the nearest emergency room.

After a 12-hour stint in a coma, Jeo was thankfully fine. His friend walked out with a fractured rib, which was a miracle.

I was broken and battered beyond belief. I had broken my back, but more so, I had broken my spirit.

Did I just get a second chance?

As you can imagine, my recovery after this accident was brutal. I'll spare you all the gory details, but I was in the hospital for almost a month, permanently attached to a morphine pump to numb away the excruciating pain.

The three months to follow were the three months that began to change my life.

In many ways, I was literally starting again: I had to develop the mental resilience to learn to walk on my own with no walker, to be able to shower with no assistance. Being able to walk to the front door unassisted was one of my goals.

It was baby steps towards getting my life back again.

But I was determined that I didn't want my OLD life back. I wanted a new one.

Was this a chance to hit the restart button? A moment to work out if everything I was doing was what I actually wanted to do?

It felt like it. Something shifted in me at that point.

I knew I had dreams, goals, wants and deep desires. But it had never seemed like there was a chance in hell that any of it was in my reach. I felt like I had wasted my life being in the Army: what was I there for? That wasn't my dream!

Since the age of seven, I always wanted to be an actor. (I still do!) I wanted to perform. So I started imagining a life where I stepped in that direction. If I wanted to be J-Lo, what was my first step going to be?

Getting rid of my ratty-ass regrowth, for one.

So, off we went to the hair salon. Afterwards I left feeling like a million bucks. I wanted to do something to help me look better, because I felt like if I looked better, I would feel better about myself. It sounds ridiculous but it's true; sometimes you need the boost of a physical 'pick me up' to get you in the right frame of mind.

That little trip to work on my outer self gave me the confidence to start working on a new goal. I wanted to be an actress, but I couldn't just expect to walk on set and book a movie star role; I had to start small. I thought modelling could be a gateway into performing.

There was a different future out there for me: I could see it. Feel it. Taste it. I slowly put myself out there – showing up, taking risks and making moves towards the life I wanted to create.

Eventually I was working full-time in my Army unit as my day job, I had started hair school at night (to help me transition out of the Army gig) and on weekends I was modelling and doing music videos in Miami. It was such a crazy time. I remember locking myself in my office and hiding from my Army supervisors so I could do a phone interview for an article in *FHM*.

It took a near-death experience to give me the push I needed to go after (what I thought were) my dreams in life.

Here's the thing: I was determined to change my life and I knew the old way wasn't working, but at that time, I wasn't doing the work that I needed to do in order to actually get different results.

My life did change and I was feeling more motivated and excited about my future than ever, but it was like this surface level of happiness.

It wasn't until 2012 when I moved to Australia that my real growth began, but I do look back on this car accident and breaking my back as my first real holy fuck, AHA moment.

It was the first experience I'd had in my life that really shook me, woke me up, screamed in my face: ERIKA! YOU HAVE ONE SHOT AT THIS LIFE!

Why are you wasting it?

You don't need to wait for shit to hit the fan to realise that your life is precious and worth living to the fullest. You don't need your life to come crashing down in an epic moment of fate or being faced with death, divorce, debt or disease before you make much needed changes. Instead of waiting for shit to happen to you, you can make shit happen *for you*.

Earlier, I briefly mentioned Virma, my amazing Army boss. When I broke my back in the car accident, she was truly an angel to me. I honestly don't know where I would be today without her.

And she was there for me a year later, when I found myself back at the hospital, this time waiting in a cold, sterile room, again wondering what the fuck was going on.

It was a Sunday afternoon. The night before, Jeo and I decided to have a house party to celebrate Cinco de Mayo. We had such an awesome time, in the safety of our own home, drinking, eating and having great conversations with our friends.

The next morning I woke up in fear, thinking I had overslept. I turned to see that Jeo wasn't in the bed next to me. I picked up my phone and saw he had called me at 1:20 am. No text, no voicemail? I quickly got up thinking he may have passed out on the couch, but he wasn't there.

I checked my house phone and noticed that the hospital had called at 7 am. I called the hospital back. I asked if they had anyone by the name of Jeovanni Lopez there and said that someone had called me at 7 am.

"Ma'am we're sorry, we can't give you information like this over the phone, it's probably best that you come in."

CONTROL ALT DELETE

After I'd been waiting for what seemed like an eternity, I looked up and noticed the double doors to the ER swing open as if it was all in slow motion.

I locked eyes with a nurse in bright blue scrubs, and then a doctor in a tan suit jacket with clipboard in his left hand.

As soon as our eyes met, their gaze dropped. The nurse spoke first. "I'm so sorry. He didn't make it."

Time stood still. I heard the words, but I couldn't comprehend what she was saying.

On Sunday, the 6th of May 2007 at 4:35 am, my husband Jeovanni Lopez had passed away while drink-driving. He veered off the road hitting a ditch and flipping his car.

To this day, this single moment has been the hardest, most excruciating thing I've ever had to live through. Not the physical abuse, not the jumping from foster home to foster home, not the sexual abuse, or being kidnapped by my father, not breaking my back or Jeo being sent to war for a year.

None of it could compare to this deep loss.

Virma had saved my life again. She came and she looked after me. She stayed with me.

I now know the universe has sent this woman to guide me because the series of events that I was about to move through, I could have never done alone.

Most of us say we could never go through something like this, but the reality is that when you are faced with these difficult times, you somehow find a way to keep showing up. You have to – you don't have a choice.

This was my rock bottom.

I had lived through so much pain and adversity and trauma, but this? This I couldn't work through. I had never known anyone who died and to have my husband be my first experience of death felt like an injustice. I felt completely trauma'd out – like, fuck me, haven't I been through enough? Now I have to deal with this, too?

The next five years were a blur. I got into relationship after relationship that didn't serve me, just so I wouldn't feel alone. I took on modelling jobs so I could feel desired, pretty and worthy.

I numbed out for the next five years of my life, trying to Control ALT Delete my past and basically doing anything I could that would make me feel less broken and damaged. I didn't want to 'deal with it', whatever that meant, because I had a deep-seeded unconscious belief that if I let myself cry too much or 'deal with his death', that I too would become bipolar like my mother – and I didn't want that to happen.

To be honest, I didn't even know how to 'deal with it'. I'm not sure if you've ever felt that way, but it's a weird space to be in. You know something's not right, you know you're not a hundred percent fulfilled and happy, yet you have no idea how to fix it, or what to do about it?

It took me countless years and hours of hard-earned personal growth and lots of blood, sweat and tears to arrive at the place I am today – happy, whole and confident. I took five key steps to build myself up from the depths of despair.

THE FIVE C'S TO BUILDING CONFIDENCE
Choice

To walk through life with confidence, first and foremost you need to acknowledge that you have choices. You have free will to *choose* what you want or don't want and whether you realise it or not, you are making dozens of choices on the daily. The question is: are the choices you're making leading you towards empowering decisions? Or have your choices been keeping you in fear?

This is the first part of creating confidence, because truly effective decision-making can only come from a place of empowering CHOICES.

Every single one of us, every single day in every single moment, has the ability to make a decision. This is one of our many choices. Choice and decision go hand-in-hand when it comes to you practising confidence.

When we aren't actively choosing to make decisions for the things that matter most to us, we end up idle. This is when we 'wish' things would change and 'hope' for more in our lives, but we haven't actually DECIDED to choose something better for ourselves.

A classic example of this is wanting to lose weight. How many of us have committed to changing the way we eat? "The diet starts on Monday," we promise, and in that moment, we are making the choice to lose weight. But when it comes to deciding what to eat for dinner on Friday night, we reach for that third slice of pizza or order another glass of wine.

In other words – the *decision* that we make doesn't line up with our *choice*.

This is also where 'procrastination station', 'analysis paralysis' and self-sabotage tend to kick in. And where we can unconsciously fall into the trap of comparison and judgment of ourselves and of others – thinking that it may be others are 'just born with self-confidence'.

In reality, it's not easier for anyone else than it is for you; they are just deciding to move through the practice. They are making choices and deciding to act on their life, instead of watching it pass by and giving reasons why it's not working out the way they wanted.

The first choice you need to make is to decide! It sounds funny, right? But honestly, that's all there is to it – instead of procrastinating on this little choice, just decide that you're going to start moving in the direction of what you desire.

Decide that you are going to finally go for and create what you want.

ACTION: What's the one decision you need to make right now?

TIP: Don't let fear get in your way – what would you love to do? Think big.

Courage

Courage is one of the most important parts of creating confidence. It is *THE* thing that gets us through uncertainty and it also goes hand-in-hand with choice – it almost feels like they happen at the same time!

The thing about courage is that it doesn't come to you unless you actually do the scary thing. In other words, you don't muster up the courage to do the courageous thing. It doesn't work like that. Instead, the courage comes AFTER you have made the choice to just go for it, regardless of the fear and the unknowing.

Just as confidence will not come until you start practising it (you don't get *confidence to be confident*), your courage won't come without you being courageous. So, what does it mean to be courageous? This is what courage is: it's when you do something, even though you are literally shitting yourself about it. I mean it, like the new definition of courage should be:

Courage: definition/noun
The feeling of pee dripping down your leg and or skid marks in your undergarments while you are doing something you are super shit scared to do.

This is courage! You are nervous. You are scared. You are freaking out. But you move forward anyway. Courage is all about you taking action, despite the fear.

It is about moving forward and making progress while you are simultaneously shitting yourself. So much fun, right?!

Sometimes, it can feel like courage is jumping off the cliff of indecision with no wings, with no parachute and no 'Plan B'.

You walk to the edge of the cliff on shaky legs, looking down, wondering what the hell will happen if you jump. If you stay perched on the edge for too long, you'll either shit yourself or talk yourself out of it.

So, you jump. Holy shit! Holy shit! Holy shit!

You're screaming as you fall, wondering if you're crazy for jumping, hoping that you grow wings before you hit the bottom.

Can a human even grow wings? Is this possible? Am I nuts?!

"I have no parachute, I have no wings, I have no safety net – BUT, I believe my wings can come. I believe that I will not fall. I believe that I can do this."

And then all of a sudden, because you have the epic self-belief and because you've burned all the boats, you've backed yourself and you've jumped, you grow wings right before you hit the bottom.

That's what courage is.

> **ACTION:** Confidence doesn't always feel good, it's hard work. What courageous thing are you willing to do today? How are you willing to show up?

> **TIP:** Stop telling yourself you're not confident. You will never have it if you keep telling yourself you lack it. Watch your words.

Create

This is about taking aligned, creative action. It's about becoming resourceful and innovative. When you create, the actions you take are in alignment with your choices, your emotions and your feelings.

What you're creating needs to feel good, exciting and inspiring. This is why step three of the practice isn't simply called 'action' – anyone can take action. But action just for the sake of action is not useful. It's not going to change your world. It's not going to help you live with vitality and purpose.

We live in a world where we're constantly trying to DO something, to hustle hard and be high-achieving action-takers. It seems like we're always taking action towards something. You may find that you get frustrated or even burnt out, and you still don't get the results you want. If this is happening, it's likely because the action you're taking isn't in alignment with what you really want to create. In fact, it is actually counterproductive.

In this step I want to invite you to move away from the idea of just 'taking massive action' and doing shit just for the sake of doing it, and I want you to make sure that everything you're doing is aligned to your values.

And so, while 'action' can be very narrow in its meaning, 'create' opens your mind to find a different angle, to find a different way, to create an opportunity, create new results – instead of finding reasons why you can't make it happen for yourself.

However, when you create, it allows you the opportunity to innovate and step into your 'make it happen' creator vibes.

ACTION: What's the ONE thing you need to act on?
The first step to get you started?

TIP: Don't get stuck in overwhelm. I am suggesting one small step.

Consider

Reflection, evaluation and perspective: that's what our fourth step, consider, is all about.

Once you take the action in step three to *create*, you'll get a result. Now, you need to pause for a moment to consider how that action went.

What was the outcome or the result of the action you took? Every time you take an action (whether it's in alignment or not) you will get feedback on your results. Was it positive? Did you succeed? Did you get the outcome you wanted? Or was the action you took no good? Did you get a shitty result, do you feel like it sucked?

This is where people may say "I failed," but I want you to consider another option here.

Whenever you take an action, whenever you DO something that doesn't work out the way you had imagined it would, you have an opportunity. I personally don't use the word fail and no, it's not because I think it's a bad word. I just believe that words have power.

Your words create your world. Language is so very important, and how you choose to speak about yourself will impact the way you think and feel, especially when you're trying to create confidence. I know that they've tried to make it cool to fail now by saying 'fail forward, fail fast'. No thank you. It feels very similar to the phrase 'fake it till you make it' – and I'd rather say, "fuck fake it, just make it!"

In order to arrive at this magical place where you are fully confident and oozing self-belief, you need to redefine what the word 'failure' means to you.

If failure to you means you failed and therefore, you're a failure and you haven't succeeded – then I want to invite you to see failure in a different light.

I want you to see failing as *learning*.

If you call it a failure there's going to be shame and all kinds of low vibe energy attached to it, but there doesn't have to be. You *are* gonna fuck some shit up – it's going to happen.

And that's a gift, because it means you get to go back and evaluate what worked and what didn't, so you learn for the next time. You get to take the L – nope, not the LOSS. The LESSON!

If I gave up public speaking because I totally bombed my first gig, I would never be the speaker I am today. But the more I fucked up (what some call fail), the more I LEARNT what I needed to: stop fidgeting, speak slower, take a deep breath before getting on stage, do a power pose. You get me?

When you don't get the result you want (aka you fail) it teaches you something and you get to consider the lesson here. What did you learn? What did that experience teach you?

Maybe you learnt that the way you went about that particular action was the wrong way. Now you can attempt it in a different way, so you LEARNT something. It's a lesson – why would you call that a failure?

Think about it: how does it feel when you fail? It sucks and it doesn't feel good at all.

It doesn't pump you up. It doesn't make you want to go and try again, that's for sure. And guess what? You have to try again every time you fall flat on your ass!

You've got to get your ass back up and go again.

This is how J-Lo, Oprah, Beyonce, and basically everybody who you think is confident does it – this is how they're confident. They fall and they fall hard. They fall publicly. But then? They get their asses back up and they keep it moving, because they've got more moves to make, more lessons to be learnt. And we can only learn these lessons by messing up and having these difficult experiences.

So, let's say you trip on rock in the fog.

You fall over.

Now you know that you shouldn't walk that way. The next step you take is in a slightly different direction, so you don't make the same mistake again

– or you get better at balancing on rocks and not falling over when you step on them.

Every time you fall, every single time that you go the wrong way or you mess up in life, it builds your resilience. It helps you create this unstoppable self-belief within you where you stop caring about the fall.

Where you know you're going to fall or you know there will be times where shit goes wrong, but you don't let that stop you.

Better yet, you get to learn from each and every one of those important experiences.

Welcome to being a human on planet earth!

This statement is true for everyone: I know I am going to fall down, hard. I know people are going to judge me from my fall. I know I'm going to judge myself. I'm going to mess up.

ACTION: What came as a RESULT of your ACTION? How did you go in the action step?

TIP: Consider you can't fail, you will only learn. You may learn that it didn't work out. Why? What did this teach you for the next time? Your results are a reflection of this practice so take a moment to consider what you learned.

Continue

This is all about momentum, baby! Step five is continue, where it all comes together: it's the 'snowball stage' of the practice.

This is also the step that connects right back into step one, choice. You see, when you're *living and breathing* the 5 Cs, then this step (continue) becomes a way of life.

It means you are committed to always going back to step one and choosing what's next, into step two to get that courage going, into step three to create the aligned action, into step four to consider your results. You evaluate, reflect and then, boom! Continue – YOU. DO. IT. ALL. AGAIN.

AND AGAIN.

AND AGAIN.

You keep it moving, that's the practice – it actually becomes one continuous movement. It happens so fast sometimes that you may not even know what step you're on. And that's why I've slowed it down and broken it into bite-sized steps for you, now you know what to do if you get stuck. You know what your next 'C' is.

The idea with this practice is that you don't stop moving through it; remember like the commitment to meditation, there is no 'arriving' at a final destination. With the 5 Cs, it's the practice itself that gets you creating confidence. If you stop, you're not in the practice anymore. So guess what? You're not gonna get better at it.

You're not going to cultivate and create confidence.

When you stop, you're no longer in creation mode. The more you continue to move forward with these five steps, the more you don't even realise that you're in a step. Continuing becomes a way of life and it keeps you in the practice of confidence, always and forever.

Why? Because it's called growth. Hopefully by now you've got your head around the idea that you will not get to a final place. You will never achieve 'confident', you'll be doing confident things. You'll be doing things that confident people do, which is making choices and decisions, mustering up some fucking courage when really you're scared as hell, putting yourself out there with your actions and evaluating how it went so that you can do it all again.

Can you see how it's a practice with no end-point? You'll always have to make another choice, get encouraged for the next scary thing, so you can take action to then ask yourself, "How was that? Okay, maybe it was shit. Let's try that again," or "That was amazing! I got this, let me keep this momentum going!"

Whether it's good, bad, or needs work, you are there showing up, and making it happen for yourself.

Continue is about being committed to moving, growing and evolving. If you stop, you don't grow. If you stop, you don't create. If you stop, choices and decisions don't get made in your life (or at least not the ones you want to be making). There's no courage being created in your world.

There's no alignment and no action being taken, no small steps towards the things that you want.

So then, you don't get what you want.

And what's worse, you may start to think, "Oh, it's because I'm not good enough."

Nope! Wrong. It's because you didn't continue to move, it's because you stopped moving.

There's no such thing as being 'wrong' or 'failing' and it's ridiculous to judge ourselves as 'not enough' just because we made a mistake.

Maybe you needed to make that mistake? Maybe you needed to learn something. I can almost guarantee that there was a lesson you needed to experience.

So, there is no end with the 5 Cs. There is no: "Yasss! I'm there. I've made it!" There's no 'making it'. It's called life. It's called growth.

You get better each and every time you try and that's the whole point – when you're in the practice of confidence, you get to keep evolving into a greater, more aligned version of yourself.

ACTION: What's your next decision? Your next action?

TIP: Confidence is a practice. Commit to daily, hourly – sometimes even moment to moment – practice.

You must CREATE your confidence.

ALONE, NOT LONELY

ANNA VON ZINNER

ANNA VON ZINNER

Anna Von Zinner is a positively determined human being.

She is a professional author, editor, writing coach and international speaker, and lives life completely unafraid. Having a stroke at 50, she found new purpose and direction in life.

Anna decided she would no longer follow the crowd and brought forward her true gifts and ability to see the world in a way that wasn't always obvious to others. She has discovered that airing her opinions and thoughts has enabled friends, colleagues and even strangers to change the way they view their worlds.

It is off the back of this that Anna launched her own freelance writing, editing and coaching business just this year.

Until early 2021, Anna worked as a corporate support person to senior administrators and on multi-million dollar projects for the Victorian State Government. Before that, she spent time working in universities and in corporate roles. Anna has a degree in communication and has seen what life is like working in many industries.

Anna has a story about everything and uses this great power to connect others through the written word. As Anna puts it, writing is her legacy.

Anna has co-authored and edited four Amazon bestsellers and regularly speaks on 'Creating Your Written Legacy' and 'The Subtle Art of the Stupid Question'.

Having a stroke does not have to be a death sentence, but the choices you make afterwards can be.

She chooses to be unafraid.

**You can contact Anna at www.annavonzinner.com
and bookannanow@gmail.com.**

To: All Staff
Subject: Corona Connections

Hi Team,

We are about to have the strangest Easter that any of us has ever had. No leaving home unless you absolutely have to for four days.

Who would have thought it?

While we all work in smaller teams, our larger team is a friendly and fun loving one. We care about and look out for one another, which is important when life is both good and bad.

A couple of weeks ago we were asked if we would like to share our mobile numbers with the rest of the team so that we could be contacted. A large number of us agreed to be on that contact list. I have now put all those numbers on one page and attached it to this email.

If you haven't seen any action from someone on Skype, Teams or email and are worried, please take the time to reach out to them. They may not feel comfortable in reaching out themselves and will appreciate you making contact. If you feel the need to speak to someone, please do; there will be no judgement

Being able to reach out and share how you feel in tough situations is a brave thing to do. Please talk to someone if you need. That is what friends and colleagues are here for.

Nobody on the planet can say that they have experienced anything like what we are going through now. This is uncharted territory. It is okay to feel unsure and uncertain about a whole range of things.

So, to lift our spirits (and to give you a sure laugh), today's song is 'Kazoos' by John Penna. I guarantee it won't be what you're expecting.

More stories and tunes next week.
Cheers,
Anna.

* * *

The Pandemic. COVID-19. Coronavirus.

What started as sharing jokes about the great toilet paper drought of 2020 and churning out loaves of baked goods, quickly erupted into global crisis. In December 2019, the world watched on as the first case of COVID-19 was discovered in Wuhan, China. We stood by as reported cases rolled in; the virus eventually taking Asia, the US and Europe. Fast forward to March 2020, and COVID had well and truly reached our Aussie shores.

COVID swept the world off its feet. Not one country, city or individual was safe from its grasp. With it came strict stay at home orders, cancelled holidays, and struggling businesses. We were propelled into a new reality without warning, as governments grappled with health policies and scientists scrambled to produce a vaccine.

The physical consequences of coronavirus were (and continue to be) serious. Without a cure, the contagion spreads like wildfire, targeting the respiratory system of one carrier to another. For some, the symptoms are mild (a sore throat and dry cough), for others: fatal. (As at August 2021, the reported COVID-19 death toll stands at over four million.)[1]

But, for all the physical costs, the mental impacts were matched. Loneliness, lethargy and insecurity became permanent fixtures in our emotional states. Thrust into uncertainty, we slowly came to terms with the ever-expanding cavern of isolation between us all. "Lockdown will only last two weeks" became, "Will we see each other for Christmas?" There was no knowing how or when things would go back to normal, or if they ever would.

THE HUMAN CONDITION

We all need connection. It is the human condition. We love to feel accepted and valued and appreciated. Even the most introverted of us requires space and support to talk things out. It is a fundamental part of who we are.

COVID robbed us of this unity. We replaced milestones with messages from afar, and face-to-face contact with sporadic Zoom calls between co-workers and virtual happy hours with friends. It didn't take long before even those things dropped off, as we each succumbed to the heavy fatigue of COVID exhaustion.

Without connection, we were lost. We were alone and flailing without anything to ground us. So much of our identity is wrapped up in our relationships with others, that we felt hollow and insignificant without them. We were left feeling more stressed, less motivated, and starved for physical touch (which, in turn, stripped us of that daily dose of oxytocin).

I could see it in my office. Pre-COVID, at least once a day, every day, each employee had the opportunity to walk past someone else's desk, say hello and ask how they were going. We weren't necessarily best friends, and often the interactions didn't delve much deeper than a comment about the weather or weekend, but we had each become accustomed to – or even reliant upon – this regular human-to-human connection. This had now been taken away.

As inconsequential as those niceties might seem, the loss impacted everyone's mental health. When we moved to a working from home (WFH) setup, there was no substitute for these simple exchanges. Without a "good morning" or "how was the weekend?" some workers could go days without any social interaction at all.

I often wondered how my peers were coping, particularly those who lived alone or in apartments. Then there were the people who had kids at home, trying to homeschool while keeping atop a full workload. They were facing the insurmountable pressure of trying to excel as a parent, employee and now, teacher, all while operating in isolation from external supports. Work was no longer just 'work'; the line between office and personal hours becoming painfully blurred. Nine to five did not exist. 'Working from home' really translated to 'living at work'.

I knew something had to be done.

CORONA CONNECTIONS

I am no stranger to being alone. Growing up, my home life was very strict, and I don't think particularly happy. Without a strong family connection, I found an escape in books. I would spend hours reading my favourite stories, making friends with the characters and immersing myself into their lives. They were my best friends; harbouring me from reality and offering me a safe place to go.

When I eventually finished school, I enrolled in a Bachelor of Business Communication, majoring in public relations (PR). A requirement of the degree was the completion of a four-week internship, and I had managed to get myself a job at Ansett Airlines in Melbourne. I'd only lived in Brisbane for five years (my parents' choice, not mine), and I couldn't wait to escape the tropical climate (that certainly didn't agree with me) and learn the PR ropes of a major airline! (Though Ansett ceases to exist today, it was once one of the heavy hitters!) So, I packed my bags (one suitcase and a sewing machine) and landed in Melbourne for Ansett's 50th anniversary celebrations.

I learnt everything I could during those four weeks: the ins and outs of media, writing and corporate communications. As it happened, the PR director became sick, and so I stayed on another four weeks. I don't want to say it was 'luck' or 'fortuitous timing' (I would never want to revel in someone else's ill health!), but it was the sign I had been looking for. When I left Brisbane, I knew I wasn't going back. The choice was between Sydney – where I had grown up or Melbourne. Melbourne won and I decided to stay permanently. Thirty-five years later, I have never looked back!

Over the course of the next three and a half decades, I worked in jobs that I loved, with people I genuinely cared for, and cared for me. I built a close-knit inner circle and moved into a home bordered by neighbours who could be relied upon for absolutely anything. The adage that 'friends are the family you choose' was the cornerstone of all my relationships, finding an immense sense of support and community in all my personal connections.

There was no doubt in my mind that interpersonal connection was intrinsically linked to a person's mental health; the feeling of togetherness created by stable relationships unparalleled. I knew that there was no match to face-to-face communication – making eye contact with a friend, or embracing a partner. However, from my early years, I had discovered the incredible power that words could have on an individual's experience of connectedness and belonging.

So, when COVID hit and we were all sent home to work, I came up with a plan. If we couldn't be physically together, perhaps we could maintain attachment through the written word. I knew that bloggers were successful in uniting their audience by sending short messages every few days, so why couldn't I do this? After all, I was a good writer and, at the very least, had nothing to lose. So, I pitched an idea to the director: every working day until our return to the office, I would email the team with an observation, quip or fun fact and include a YouTube link to a piece of music that reflected whatever I wrote about. With his approval, I sent the first email to my colleagues in our team.

To: All Staff
Subject: Corona Connections

Hi Team,

I'm in my fourth week now of being at home. For most of you, it will be your third and you may be finding it a little difficult.

I love being at home. But, I have been thinking about what I can do to keep us connected as a team and enjoying work (and life in general) in these difficult times.

So, I've had an idea! (I can see some of you cringing!)

Before I started work at the DOJ (as it was called then) I worked at La Trobe University for seven years. For two of those, I was captain of a team in the Global Corporate Challenge – a fitness challenge aimed at increasing wellness at work. In our last year, my team of seven agreed that we would aim for ten million steps over the 16 weeks of the challenge.

As captain I had to find ways of keeping my team motivated and moving. Something I did that was really well received (and ended up being shared across the five La Trobe Victorian campuses) was send the team a daily email with a link to a positive, inspiring song.

So, what I am going to do every workday from now until we go back to our desks is send an email to our team with a YouTube link to a good song for moving to. I'll also share some of the work at home tips that I see popping up in my social media feeds with the aim of trying to get your butts off your seats for at least a few minutes a day.

Because you are at home, you can sing and dance along, march on the spot, wave your arms around, dance with your kids, partner, or pets – just get off your chair for a few minutes and move!

If you have a suggestion for a song you would like on the playlist, send me an email and I'll include it. If nobody responds, I'll just link what I think is appropriate. A word of warning: my music tastes are pretty broad!

Without further ado here's our first song, which just has to be MC Hammer's 'U Can't Touch This'.

Have some safe fun peeps.
Cheers,
Anna

My strategy in writing these pieces every day was to compose something engaging and not too specific. Times were hard for everyone. We didn't need someone preaching work rules or business ethics. We all knew that stuff. What was needed was something to take the reader's mind away from what they were doing for a few minutes; sometimes make them laugh, sometimes make them think.

I wrote about anything and everything: the leaves on the ground, the mushrooms in the grass, my cats, my neighbourhood. Some days, I wrote about the stupidest things, like how I painted the tiles in my bathroom and that it was a disaster. On others, I covered more useful content, like tips and tricks for working from home and how to stay sane during lockdown. I tried to keep it light and exciting.

The feedback I got was overwhelming. My emails gave people something to look forward to. It gave my colleagues a reason to stop what they were doing and take a break – this was the only pause some of them actually took from work.

Even better, it gave us all something to talk about together. The channel of communication was open for everyone to comment and converse with one another. It created a relaxed forum to discuss our life happenings, rather than the rigid conversations over Teams and Zoom that had been focused on professional qualms and queries.

Of course, I can't speak for everyone else in my team, but Corona Connections provided me with huge emotional relief. I immediately felt less isolated, stressed and disorganised; things that had started to creep in since I began working from home four weeks prior. It wasn't the same as seeing everyone's faces every day, but it was enough to provide a sense of comradery and togetherness.

We are now in the second half of 2021 and the virus is not going anywhere anytime soon. Working from home is a reality that many of us will be facing well into the future, if not forever. It is important that we continue to place just as much importance on proactive communication to safeguard us all from the effects of loneliness and isolation.

The Black Dog Institute has a helpful checklist to support the mental health for those working from home.[2] As well as staying connected to co-workers, some tips to reduce psychological stress include sticking to a routine, setting up a dedicated workspace, and switching off digital devices to unwind.[3]

Maintaining strong physical health is also key in sustaining a positive mindset. Exercise has been shown to "improve mental health by reducing anxiety, depression, and negative mood and by improving self-esteem and cognitive function. [It] has also been found to alleviate symptoms such as low self-esteem and social withdrawal."[4] Even if you get out of the house for just 30 minutes to take a brisk walk, your mind will thank you for it.

Similarly, eating a clean diet and getting enough rest will do wonders for your mental health. Incorporating more fresh vegetables, raw foods and lean proteins into your meals will keep your body in shape and your mind clear. We have all heard of the dreaded 'COVID kilos'. Try to manage emotional eating by consuming food mindfully and minimising stressors.

To: All Staff
Subject: Corona Connections

Hi Team,

Today I want to remind you all about staying physically well, which is more than just staying home and maintaining social distance.

Make sure you are eating well. Being at home lends itself to creating some bad food habits. Be strong and make sure you stick to a healthy diet that will leave you feeling good as well as boosting your immune system.

Make time to get into the fresh air and enjoy the sunshine before the cooler weather really hits Melbourne. Ten to 15 minutes of sunlight on your skin every day will give your Vitamin D levels a boost and make you feel better.

Try to take some exercise every day. Walking around the block or gardening during work breaks are great ways to build and maintain your fitness levels. Not everyone is interested in setting up home gyms or cycling every day. Any exercise that raises your heart rate and makes you sweat is considered healthy.

For me, you know I like music. But most of you won't know that I am a huge fan of hardcore techno (amongst a lot of things)! My favourite artist in this genre is German band Scooter, who are what is referred to as 'happy hardcore' with a 4-beat bouncy, get up and move pulse. So, today your tune is 'Maria, (I like it LOUD)' by Scooter.

Turn up the volume, find your space, and jump around with me. I'll be back tomorrow with something totally different!

Stay safe,
Anna

* * *

A FRIEND IN NEED IS A FRIEND INDEED

For many of us, we regularly refuse support until we are without option. Rather than asking for a hand, we struggle and make do as best we can, fearful that reaching out will make us appear 'weak' or render us an 'imposition'. Sometimes, we might even put off seeking support out of fear of being rejected, which we consider to be 'embarrassing'. It isn't until we are completely incapacitated that we reluctantly accept the help that is available to us.

To put it bluntly – this makes no sense.

Imagine you have a friend who is struggling to juggle work, study and her family. She has a meeting late one evening and is unable to pick up the kids from school. She asks if you could do it. What do you say?

I'm guessing your response would be something along the lines of "Of course – anything I can do to help," just like I imagine most of us would offer any type of practical assistance to our friends without second thought. We like to provide support because it makes us feel good and gives us purpose and fulfilment. On top of this, society tells us that offering help is the right thing to do. So, if we know that *we* are willing to help others, why is it so hard to accept that others would want to help us?

Though we might not judge others who seek support, when it comes to our own problems, we assume that they are not significant enough to warrant another person's attention. After all, everyone has issues, why would anyone besides you have the time to worry about yours?

We are seemingly unable to accept that asking for help is not something to feel ashamed about. From a young age, we are taught that working independently, thinking innovatively and problem solving creatively are all signposts of a strong and intelligent person with a resilient mental fortitude. Asking for help therefore seems like a deviation from what we are supposed to do. It makes us feel that we are not capable enough to deal with problems and that there is something wrong with us. This could not be further from the truth.

In 2013, I had a stroke. I was in hospital for five days and when I came out, my brain was completely scrambled. It was like my head was filled with water with a few balls and rods bobbing about inside. My brain regarded everything I did as new even If I had done it a billion times before. I understand now why babies sleep so much! It was beyond exhausting. Talk about sensory overload!

But, because I am stubborn, I made a decision: I was not going to be victim to my unfortunate circumstances. An inconvenient stroke wasn't going to rob me of my fierce independence. I was going to live like I always had – alone – and that wasn't going to change. I would continue to do things as I always had: on my own.

See, the problem with this logic was that when you have a stroke, it is virtually *impossible* to complete your day-to-day living totally on your own. Simple tasks like washing the dishes or walking to the end of the driveway become overwhelmingly difficult. Then there are the harder chores, like going to the shops, which are completely out of the question without assistance.

I had to get real and accept my new reality. It wasn't like my family cared enough to come and check on me, so the typical first port of call was not an option. I *did* have an amazing group of friends and some truly incredible neighbours, but I feared the burden would become too great and they would grow tired of my relentless neediness.

I really struggled with this crossroads; the fear of overwhelming my supports at odds with my desperate need for help. In the end, I eventually sucked it up and sought aid from my nearest and dearest. I'm not going to lie, it was hard for me to ask and honestly, I hated doing it. It was almost defeating to feel so helpless.

No surprises as to what happened next. My friends and neighbours were all too keen to offer whatever support they could. "What can I grab you from the shops? Can I cut your lawn?" They were all too generous. There was always someone to offer a hand no matter what I needed or the time of day.

To learn that you are not alone is quite incredible. I knew I had some amazing people in my life, but to see my friends and neighbours rally behind me was overwhelming. Enjoying my own company and spending time by myself did not mean I was isolated, quite the opposite in fact. When I needed help, I had an incredible support system at my disposal. I wasn't an imposition;

I was a valued part of my social circle. I deserved support from my friends, just like they did from me. It was a two-way street.

Fast forward to 2020, and this lesson was pertinent as ever. Here we were, in the thick of a global health crisis, yet more alone than we ever had been. We had the helplines and knew the mental health policies, but without interpersonal support we struggled to maintain any semblance of a cheerful life. We didn't know how to put up our hands and ask for help, and if we did, we *certainly* didn't want to. Just like I had in 2013, society needed to get on board with seeking support by removing the stigma of reaching out and obliterating the fear of being vulnerable.

Of course, there were some people who never felt comfortable reaching out, no matter how much we encouraged them to. For example, in my office a large portion of my co-workers were male. For whatever reason, this *generally* discouraged them from reaching out (at least as much as their female counterparts). Similarly, I found that the older workers were less able to communicate how they were feeling, whereas the youngens were more open in seeking support. It was up to us to make that first step in bridging the communication gap.

As an office, we needed to remind every employee that it wasn't just acceptable, but that it was *preferable* that they reach out. If someone hadn't been as active on emails or Zoom, we made it a priority to check in on that person privately (and tactfully). The responsibility was on our team to create a supportive environment, and it was up to us to recognise the signs. After all, if our workplace was not an empathetic space, how could we expect anyone to actually come to us if they were feeling down?

This extended to each of our personal lives. For me, I regularly made sure that I checked in on loved ones and those who I knew might be doing it tough (whether it be financially, socially, or health wise).

I think we can all agree that asking someone to reach out in times of trouble seems like a kind thing to do. However, we need to make sure that when we ask people to use us as support, that we are adopting the right practices if they decide to take us up on the offer. These include:

• using correct listening practices, such as active listening and empathetic response

• offering support, not advice

- not minimising another person's hardship

- being available and showing up.

As hard as it was for me to reach out back in 2013, I now know that if I need something, to go and ask. After all, what's the worst that can happen? Maybe somebody says, "Sorry, I can't do it now" or "No, I don't want to." You know what, that's alright! Not everybody wants or can do everything at once!

That's the importance of fostering relationships when you are well; if something happens, you've got somebody that you can turn to when you're not so well. I guess we all like to think that we're independent and always will be. But it doesn't always work out that way. This was a huge learning curve for me.

THE SILVER LININGS

Obviously, COVID-19 had some detrimental impacts on our collective mental and physical health. After all, by definition a pandemic is a disease that is "prevalent throughout … the whole world."[5] However, for all the doom and gloom, there have been a few silver linings to come out of all of this.

1. **Increased awareness around mental health**

   There is still a long way to go in relation to mental health in Australia. However, it is undeniable that as a community we have become more in tune with one another's psychological needs in the wake of coronavirus. The shared experience of the pandemic has encouraged us to band together, creating a sense of social cohesion and unity. We are more consciously kind, empathetic and available to listen and learn from each other's struggles.

2. **Increased access to health services**

   This is a big one. How often have you had to skip out of work early just to see your GP or book in with a therapist? Since COVID, more and more health services have started offering telehealth consults, meaning you can attend on your physician without even stepping foot in the practice. The costs of these consultations can also be much lower than face-to-face appointments.

   For a lot of us, the biggest deterrent of attending a psychologist is the cost. As a direct response to coronavirus, in August 2020 the Australian Government announced that it would increase the total number of sessions that could form part of a Mental Health Care Plan by ten. This means that Australians can now "access 20 Medicare subsidised psychological therapy sessions"[6] per calendar year.

3. More inclusive fitness industry

Gone are the days of rocking up to the gym at 5:30am to fight over the only available StairMaster. Since COVID, the fitness industry has been completely transformed; no longer do we need a fancy gym membership or expensive personal trainer to stay in shape.

Classes ranging from Pilates, to HIIT, to weights (and *everything* in between) now saturate the internet. There are countless free or low cost options available online so that everyone has the opportunity to work out how they want, where they want, when they want.

The increased accessibility of fitness programs has opened up the industry to many people who otherwise felt excluded from participating in the traditional gym or group class structure. Those with limited disposable income or busy work schedules can now achieve their fitness goals in a way that suits them.

This has spurred a shift in what fitness actually looks like. No longer reserved for the ultra-thin and overtly bulky, fitness is now centred around being *genuinely* healthy, with particular focus on exercising for mental health, rather than to achieve a 'bikini body'. Walking, stretching and low-to-moderate activities like gardening and cleaning are all heralded as great ways to keep our bodies active and fit.

4. Ability to work from home

To: All Staff

Subject: Corona Connections

Hi Team,

Maintaining mental health is vital at any time. But now that we are asked to live and work in one space – our homes – how are we supposed to get away from work?

About ten years ago, I was working very long hours in a demanding Executive Assistant role. My workload was overwhelming, and I eventually reached the point where I burnt out.

When this happened, one of the best pieces of advice ever given to me was "don't take your work home." I have lived by that piece of advice ever since.

But, what do I do now?…

* * *

No one is denying the struggles that working from home can bring. We lived through them in 2020 and a lot of us are still battling them today. But for many, not having to attend the office every day is a *godsend*.

Arguably, working from home frees up a lot of time. We are spared the hours commuting to and from the office, visiting clients face-to-face, and attending meetings in person. Similarly, our painstaking morning rituals – selecting the outfit, painting the face, styling the hair – are all discarded.

During COVID, WFH gave us an extra hour (usually more) per day that we could dedicate to exercising, cooking, working on personal development, or catching up on sleep. For those with families, they were able to adopt a better lifestyle, spending more time with their kids and partners.

This had wide reaching health impacts, with employees feeling more physically and mentally fit. For example, working from home meant that instead of confining lunchtime options to the takeaway joint across the road, we had the time and space to prepare a nutritious meal with ingredients from our own pantries. Similarly, rather than starting and finishing work in the dark without reprieve, we were able to structure our days to allow for a sunny walk in the park during the day. These simple changes kept us in better physical shape, as well as left us feeling more focused, calm and productive.

5. Easier to obtain supplies

Though lockdowns saw us all scrambling for that last pack of Sorbent 2ply, it also opened up and normalised shop delivery and click and collect services. This was a welcomed development for disabled, elderly, ill, and time poor people, who were no longer forced to battle the masses for their supplies. This also eased some of the strain on high density areas (like shopping centres).

6. A healthier environment (therefore a healthier us)

Humans are like environment kryptonite. From our transportation networks to our large-scale factories, the pollution we omit into the atmosphere is incredible. So, when COVID came along and put the world into lockdown, the earth had a chance to rejuvenate.

During 2020, we saw a global increase in air and water quality, as well as a reduction in harmful emissions (such as carbon dioxide and nitrous oxides).[7] For example, "the lockdowns reduced the emissions of nitrous oxides by 20% to 30% in China, Italy, France, Spain, and by 77.3% in São Paulo, Brazil. Similarly, the particulate matter level has been reduced from 5–15% in Western Europe, to 200% in New Delhi, India, which in turn has enhanced the air quality in a never-seen manner in recent times."[8] We witnessed the earth starting to heal, as fish returned to their Venetian canals, and blue painted Beijing skies.

The quality of our environment has an undoubted impact on our health, with "prolonged exposure to air pollution caus[ing] chronic inflammation and an increased risk of chronic respiratory disease,"[9] and poor water contributing to the transmission of disease. During COVID, these threats were reduced.

CONNECTION IS EVERYWHERE

As uncertainty continues to plague our lives, we must keep seeking connection. But that doesn't mean you have to be the loudest person in the room, or the first to put up your hand to host Zoom trivia. Connection is different for everyone. Yes, I love my friends and neighbours, and *yes,* I missed my daily chats with co-workers, but I found my connection in writing. Writing is what kept my mental health in check and my spirits high. (In fact, in early 2021 I left the office life behind to focus on my own writing, editing and coaching business!)

Perhaps you prefer to connect with friends through social media, or you enjoy bonding with family over a mutual hobby. Maybe you would rather spend time connecting with yourself, either through meditation or by embracing your feelings and practising self-compassion. However you feel connected, it is important to keep pursuing these avenues so that you can be the happiest and healthiest version of yourself possible.

Who knows, you might come out of COVID better than you started!

LOSE YOU TO FIND ME

JAYNE CRAIG

Y SHIFT

JAYNE CRAIG

Who is your real soulmate? Well, according to Jayne Craig, the answer is *you*.

With a penchant for all things witchy and wonderful, Jayne grew up immersed in the spiritual world. But as she progressed through the motions of daily life – from careers to kids – this side of her slowly faded.

It wasn't until she found herself solo parenting in her thirties, that Jayne began to suffer acute anxiety, stress and overwhelm as she drifted further and further from her authentic life. Though she battled on as best she could, Jayne was forced to take action when, one day, her life was suddenly turned upside down. That's when her rebirth began.

Beginning her career as a nanny and then an early childhood teacher, Jayne eventually made the switch to permaculture design; rekindling her love of growing medicinal herbs for use in healing teas. Despite her mounting interest in the practice over the years, it wasn't until Jayne became a mother that she really started researching, learning and applying the principles of holistic health.

After studying Naturopathy and Herbal Medicine, Jayne began working as a holistic health practitioner and coach, helping others as well as herself. Jayne is also qualified in Aromascience and Postnatal Doula and has over 25 years' experience in tarot reading and earth based spirituality.

Jayne is now known as a wellness witch. Her work fuses practical skills and holistic health knowledge with ritual and spiritual coaching. Jayne is passionate about supporting and empowering women as they journey back home to their most authentic aligned selves and rediscover their own inner magic and medicine.

Jayne is currently in the process of publishing her first book, *Magic and Medicine* with Dean Publishing. In Jayne's book you will discover additional holistic health advice, wisdom, and spiritual guidance.

You can connect with Jayne at www.magicandmedicine.co.nz or @magicandmedicine_ on Instagram.

*"We delight in the beauty of the butterfly, but rarely admit
the changes it has gone through to achieve that beauty."*
Maya Angelou

My life today looks nothing like I thought it would.

I thought I would be married and parenting my children with their father.

I thought I had to settle for whatever came my way.

I thought that it was normal to always look at life, sigh and think, *is this all there is?*

I thought my anxiety was something I would always live with and struggle to manage.

I thought daily panic attacks were my normal.

I thought I was broken.

For a while, I also thought I would die.

Instead, I now find myself living in perhaps the most exciting, magical and creative phase of my life.

I am a single mother to four incredible teens.

I am raising them on my own terms.

My house is filled with humour, love, and is an oasis of calm.

I wake up every morning and get to create the kind of day I want to experience.

My work revolves entirely around supporting others and being of service – this fills my cup like nothing else. I've met the most incredible people and written my first book!

Best of all, the anxiety and depression that crippled me and haunted my daily life has been relegated to the past.

The anxiety that spiralled into a dark depression and was once a controlling factor in my life, is now a memory. This was a huge part of my journey that helped me to grow and asked me to heal.

My name is Jayne, I am a Wellness Witch and this is the story of my journey back home to myself.

* * *

In today's world, mental health issues – stress, overwhelm, and anxiety – have reached pandemic levels. The western world is so rich in resources and ways to seek connection, and yet its members increasingly feel isolated and alone. We put so much pressure on trying to *do* everything and *be* everywhere, that we are left reeling from life's never-ending saga of to-do lists and calendar appointments. We habitually forget (or ignore) our psychological needs in place of more urgent tasks, prioritising others' desires above our own. We seldom create our own happiness, and instead rely on our partners, friends, children and parents to provide it for us.

Stillness and listening to our bodies and intuition is beginning to become a lost art. We shrug off the signals our mind and body send us, pushing our inner knowing down the priority ladder, to be dealt with at another time when its more convenient or less confronting to look at. Often that time will never come, and our innate wisdom will have to scream at us through the mess of our life as it falls down around us. Sometimes the only way to break through is to first break down.

Over the next few pages, I will share a snippet of my story with you to prove that no matter what the universe throws at you, there is *always* a path through the mess. I will share with you my journey and some of the practices that got me through my darkest days, so that I could be reborn into the woman I was always destined to be.

THE CATALYST

"It is over," he said. "We will never be husband and wife again."

Something within me broke. I split apart at the seams – the pain of my emotions spilling out of me. I couldn't stop crying even if I wanted to. Sobs wracked my body as the tears came so thick and fast that I could scarcely catch my breath. I struggled to drag myself from my foetal position on the carpet to throw up the rising bile in my mouth into the toilet. The pain in my heart was all consuming. I wanted to die.

My husband had left me and our four children to live overseas with his girlfriend. Looking back, I shouldn't have been surprised, neither one of us had been living our best lives for a long time. But, something about hearing the words come out of his mouth – the finality – broke me in ways I still struggle to describe. This was a relationship I had put my all into. My heart, my time, my energy, my entire identity was wrapped up in being this man's wife and the mother of his children. I had put him first over and over again.

Why wouldn't he do the same for me?

Did our twenty years together mean nothing? What about the family we had made, the memories we had created, the future we had plotted? Was I such a shit wife and mother that it could all be tossed aside for someone new?

I felt I was nothing without my husband. The shock of him leaving abruptly and moving on to another relationship so quickly left me reeling. I struggled to make sense of any of it. I realise now that it wasn't just the shock of losing this relationship, but also the shock of losing the story I was telling in my head (everything was all right, we could work through anything, our relationship was great!).

There was no hiding from reality anymore. I was in deep pain mourning the loss of a man I thought was my soulmate, as well as the fairytale I had been creating about him in my head.

I spent weeks crying. My anxiety quickly spiralled into depression. I couldn't sleep, I couldn't think clearly. My whole body hurt from the grief I felt. I began stockpiling pills and researching what combination of meds could end my life. I made it through each day with two thoughts: the determination to push through for my children, and the knowledge that if the pain got too great, there was always a way out.

For the next year I waded through the muck of depression, contemplating suicide and battling rage that at times made me so irrational and bitter I didn't recognise myself. Then I realised the truth: I had been given an opportunity to be reborn and find my way back home to myself.

ACKNOWLEDGING THE PAST

The seeds that are sown in childhood have an enormous impact on our adult lives. Every trivial event and inconsequential comment that we experience as a child eventually finds its way into our adult psyche, exposing itself through our thoughts, behaviours and actions. To fully unlock why we are the way that we are, we must first look to – and then come to terms with – our upbringing.

Growing up, I was a creative child. I loved reading books and writing stories – anything that took me out of my physical space and into my world of imagination. I devoured mythological texts, books on ancient history and folk and fairy tales, often spending entire days curled up reading in a chair. I couldn't get enough.

My dad was a bank manager, so my family moved around a lot – never spending more than three to five years in the one place. Because of this, I attended a total of seven schools. This was hard for me. I was reserved and shy and I found constantly being 'the new girl' exceptionally challenging. I felt like I was always on the back foot: what was 'cool' in one school was never the same as the next. Moving around so much made me dependent on my parents to accept and validate me. I didn't necessarily have access to a secure friend network, so I relied on mum and dad to give me direction. I felt like every move asked me to give away parts of myself and look to others for opinions on how I should be, how to act, what to wear, and what was acceptable in order to fit into each new place.

When I turned 15, I got a job and suddenly had my own money to spend. I wandered through the shops in town, in search of things to buy – the money burning a hole in my pocket. That's when I discovered it. Down a side street was a small shop. From the open door poured the earthy scent of burning incense. Stained glass and feathery ornaments shone behind its windows, where books, jewellery, and bowls of crystals were stacked on shelves and counters inside. I had never experienced anything like it! I spent my entire paycheck in one fell swoop.

I delved head first into this spiritual realm. It felt so familiar to me, yet was completely unlike anything I had ever experienced. I visited the tiny shop every week – spending most of my pay and time there. I cobbled together my own views on spirituality and started to find my voice and express myself. I felt like I was discovering a whole new authentic me! But, then when I was 16, we moved again.

With the new move came a new school. I was at an awkward age where I didn't really want to interact with anyone. I resented the town I found myself in and missed my friends. I spent a lot of my time sleeping in my room, dreaming the days away. Looking back, I was depressed.

I was painfully lacking in confidence. I had already learnt not to trust myself. My teenage years is where I began to doubt my intuition and override the signals my nervous system would send me, in favour of following someone else's advice.

These small events set in motion a path and precedent for doubting myself and settling for less as an adult.

The one thing that kept me grounded throughout this time was a spiritual hub in the middle of town. I spent a lot of time there, learning to meditate, having my cards read, borrowing books and attending talks on different new age topics. I soaked it up like a sponge. Within this realm of spirituality, I felt like myself.

PERFECT WIFE, IMPERFECT LIFE

I was just 17 when I met my future (now ex) husband and father to my children.

I had never had a serious boyfriend before, and found his attention flattering and all consuming. We developed a friendship and then a relationship.

He was seven years my senior with two young children and his own business already thriving. He seemed to have it all together and offered me the stability and acceptance I craved. Naturally, I considered him more adult and experienced. He had the knowledge I simply didn't. He was older, smarter, wiser, stronger. I respected his judgement above all else. I diverted to him on almost everything.

Like a lot of young love, what started out as a fun romance quickly evolved into serious commitment. We took overseas trips together, bought a house, a cat and a dog. I became his wife and the mother to his children. Sounds perfect, right?

Wrong.

You see, in the few short years that we had spent building a life together, all my adult learning, first experiences, and happiest memories became attached to him. I gave parts of myself away to become more palatable. I put stock in his opinions over mine until I had completely eroded my sense of self. I was no longer well rounded and whole.

I didn't see that the codependency I developed did us both a disservice. It wasn't healthy for me. Emotionally, I had stopped growing. It was also an unfair burden for him to carry as a husband, to be the one person expected to fulfil all my needs. In trying to make myself the perfect wife – agreeable and supportive – I didn't realise how inauthentic I was being, or that what I was doing was actually manipulative. I wasn't being my true self. Instead, I was offering up a persona I thought would create the stable loving relationship I craved.

We travelled overseas to a small island in the Pacific Ocean for holidays until my husband decided he wanted to make the move permanently. I had never enjoyed my island holidays, but I didn't want to stand in the way of his dreams. So, we packed up what we could and settled into island living.

My first year was spent living in a farmhouse with questionable internet, no television, and no car. Aside from the two house girls, I saw no one but my infant son while my husband was at work. I was desperately isolated and lonely – missing my home, family and friends in New Zealand.

We moved a few more times around the island, until we bought a house by the sea. Over the years I gave birth to our second child and a few years later our twins.

I was extremely unhappy during this phase of my life and regularly woke up screaming "let me out of here!" My husband always soothed me with the promise we would move back home in six months. But first, he just had to close that deal, finish that project, or make X amount of money.

When the twins were two years old and my eldest was ready to start school, my husband eventually agreed that we would all move back home – myself and the children first, then he would follow six months' later, once he had sold the house and wrapped up his businesses.

I was so relieved to be back home! But soon I was faced with the reality of having to be the only parent at home with four young children while my husband worked overseas.

It was around this time that I started noticing some bizarre things happening to my body. For example, when I was out walking the dogs and pushing the kids in the pram, I would suddenly get tight chested, light-headed and a feeling of panic would wash over me. I had no idea what it meant. Was I ill? Broken? Faulty? Then came the worst thought of all: if something happened to me, what would happen to the kids?

I tell you what it meant – my inner wisdom was talking to me through anxiety.

I wasn't living the life I desired, and my subconscious knew it. My inner wisdom had made my anxiety so crippling that I couldn't ignore the signals. My body knew what I needed, even when my conscious mind didn't.

My anxiety wasn't because my nervous system was broken, it was because I was disconnected from myself and from life.

I had been essentially left to raise the children on my own while my husband worked on his business and took solo trips around the world. I was left playing a supporting role, watching someone else chase their dreams while I had very few of my own.

But, of course, I didn't recognise any of this back then.

I went for a checkup and the doctor told me I was experiencing anxiety and put me on SSRIs. The anxiety got worse – heart racing, stomach churning, tingling in my hands and feet. I began experiencing intense panic attacks, so I added valium to my prescription. I felt like I was going to pass out as dark panic roared its way up my body and closed in around my head. A couple of times I did pass out, which only made me *more* anxious. I was worried of fainting and losing control when out in public or driving a car. So, I started going out less and less. I was isolating myself without even realising it.

Struggling to parent alongside returning to full time study (I was training to become a Naturopath, in a bid to help my mental health) and running a household on my own, I called my husband in January 2017 and told him he had to move back home. Three months later, he emailed me stating he wanted a divorce. Three days after that came an email saying he had met and was dating someone. Soon after, he told me she had moved in.

Queue, Jayne in a heap on the floor, crying into the carpet.

What was I going to do? How could I ever get through this? Wasn't I stronger than this woman I'd become, who fell apart because a man didn't want to love her anymore?

Ironically, it was these kind of outer body observations that snapped me out of my depression. I recognised this voice, from long ago – the voice of guidance was my higher self. I realised I was in a new phase of life. I now had the opportunity to live a life entirely by my own design.

SEARCHING FOR JAYNE
Step One: Mindset Manifesting

First thing was first – I needed to start working on my mindset. Serendipity led me to finding a life coach who helped me peer into the cracks of my marriage that I had previously glossed over. She helped me pull past hurts and self-destructive beliefs out of the closet that I had firmly locked in. I rebuilt and nurtured my nervous system, which was shot after years of anxiety and depression. I connected with some of the most incredible women and men who have enriched my life more than I could ever dream. Best of all, I reinvested my energy into the aspect of my life that had never left me, even when I neglected it: *my connection to spirit.*

Because I was working on myself, loving myself, and rebuilding my relationship with myself, I started feeling a renewed sense of interest in myself and my old spiritual beliefs bubbled back to the surface. I threw myself into developing a daily spiritual practice that became the backbone of all that I do today. Occasionally, I would stop for a few days to wallow and feel sorry for myself (I think it's important to allow yourself these dips and not beat yourself up), but day by day my mind cleared and my spirit grew stronger.

I worked on myself nonstop. Things that used to really bother me weren't a big deal anymore. I'd catch myself if I got too involved in worrying about other people's thoughts, if I was getting stuck in circulating thoughts, if I was too self-critical or was stuck in a 'poor me' mentality. I continually pushed myself out of my comfort zone and tried things I had previously told myself I couldn't do.

About a year into intensively working on me, I found myself smiling and singing to myself as I went about my day. It dawned on me that I really liked myself. In fact, I loved and adored the person I had become.

Write It Out

Journaling is a great way to manifest a new mindset. You could begin writing in a notebook or on your laptop, or record a voice note or video of yourself. It doesn't matter what option you choose. The point is to record your thoughts so that you have a way of documenting your journey. This will allow you to do two things:

1. You will be able to see growth. When you look back and see the reminders of what you used to do and think, you will see how you have evolved.

2. You will be able to see repeating patterns in your behaviour, thinking and the situations you find yourself in. You will also be able to identify the ways your inner self is trying to get your attention, either by showing you shadow aspects of yourself, or through small coincidences.

Having a safe space to write out your thoughts and fears is a huge healing step that is often underestimated. The more that you can journal, the more deeply you will connect with yourself. As soon as you write, you won't just be recording your thoughts and feelings, you will also be making space for your intuition – your higher self – to write back.

Gently allow your inner voice to answer any questions you have. Ask what you need and watch for answers as you write. Perhaps it's a nap, a hot drink, or a walk in nature. Just write and allow your pen to flow – you may be surprised by the answers that come up.

As you write, allow yourself to release all the stories, emotions – everything. Writing is very cathartic. It allows our brains to organise and make sense of our struggles and emotions by putting them into story form. It is also important to allow yourself to tell your own story. There is huge power in telling your perspective and validating the experiences you have had.

This is your judgement free space to write and let go; to nurture and love yourself the way you truly deserve. This is where you can start to reconnect the threads of your intuition and higher self and stitch them back into the fabric of your life.

Step Two: Find and Follow Your Intuition

We are taught from a young age to look to others for answers. Every time a parent told us to deny our emotions – to stop that tantrum, to be the good girl – we were taught how to act. We look to our teachers to tell us how to think and to healthcare providers to tell us all the ways our bodies are broken. Most of us forget to look within first.

Tapping into your intuition should be part of your daily practice. It's your innate guidance system, and for most people, is under-utilised. Much like strengthening any muscle in the body, your intuition will get stronger the more you use it.

Wise Woman Meditation

Meditation is a great way to provide space in your mind for clarity, calm and to hear your wisdom.

Get comfortable, put on some gentle music and close your eyes. Imagine you are walking down a hallway. In your hand there is a key. This key can be as ornate or simple as you like. As you walk, you reach a door. Take a moment to take in its details. Is it simple and modern? Is it old? What material and colour is it?

Notice the keyhole. Put the key in and turn it to open the door. As the door swings open, step over the threshold and into a room in which you feel utterly at home and at peace. Let the door close gently behind you. Take a moment to gaze around your surroundings. What shape is the room? Is it modern and airy? Cosy and cottage like? Form the room into the kind of space you would love to spend time in.

Once your space is fully formed, take a seat in one of your chairs. As you recline, you hear footsteps. Your guide is coming to greet you. Allow yourself to receive your guide without any preconceived ideas. Notice what your guide looks like. Do they have a clear form? Are they human? Are they male or female? How are they dressed?

As your guide gives you a welcoming embrace, notice the comforting energy they give off. Feel yourself relax as you know you are completely and utterly safe. This is your inner sanctum; it is only for you.

Now that you and your guide have greeted each other, you start to tell them your problem. Listen to the wisdom your guide gives back to you. Let your guide give you the healing and medicine you need.

When your guide has finished, you have received what you needed. Thank your guide and let them know you'll be back to visit them as often as you can. Stand up and exit through the same door you entered and put the key in your pocket for safekeeping. Walk slowly back down the hall. As you do this, start to gently move your physical body and come back to the here and now. When you are ready, take a few deep breaths and open your eyes.

Step Three: Spirituality is the Bedrock of Being

I have always been spiritual. I still have books I purchased 25 years ago – books on crystal healing, past lives, Native American spirituality, witchcraft and magical beings. They helped shape my beliefs and expand my mind.

My spiritual practice has become the bedrock for everything I do. Creating sacred space, celebrating life with ritual, leaning into my intuition, and developing a relationship with spirit was vital to raising me out of a dark, suicidal depression and setting me on the path of self-healing and self-growth.

I practice a very grounded type of spirituality. I believe that we are our own temples. We don't need the trappings of ritual or a special building to connect with the divine, because we have that connection within us all the time. However, it is true that a sacred space or ritual can help us move more quickly from mundane thinking and into a more expansive spiritual mindset.

Step Four: Your Home is Your Haven

Haven. That word, concept, has always drifted in my thoughts. Perhaps it is because as a child I moved to a new town and school every three to five years. Maybe it's because as a second generation New Zealander, I felt a disconnect from my homeland and roots.

When I was training as a teacher, I was introduced to the word *Tūrangawaewae*, which means a place to stand, or a place or places where we feel especially empowered and connected. *Tūrangawaewae* is our foundation, our place in the world, our home. That was the feeling I longed for.

As an adult, I want to generate this feeling for myself and my children. I want to create my home, my haven, my place to stand. We spend so much of our lives in our homes. Under its roof we laugh, cry, argue, and make love. Our home is a container for our lives, yet we often treat it like it is nothing more than a dumping ground for our possessions. Our homes can become messy, strewn with objects and collecting dust as we eat, work, sleep, repeat.

I want to invite you to look at your home as I do – like a living being. When I clean my house, I clean with intention. I infuse the house with love, weaving my thoughts and wishes for joy and protection as I wipe down surfaces and clean the floors. I believe that if I treat my home with care, it will shelter me with care in return. Every few days, I clean my floors with a spiritual cologne or essential oils, to not only make my floor shine, but to do double duty and invite good energy in and seal my intentions. Every day, I open windows to let out any stagnant energy from the day before. Even in winter I open the windows for a few minutes before I turn the heat on.

Your home is your sacred space. It is a reflection of you, so treat it accordingly. Fill it with colours, objects and scents that make you feel happy and inspired. You don't have to spend a lot of money or follow the latest interior design trends to make your space beautiful. Bring nature in with potted plants, flowers, pinecones, feathers or seashells. Allow your personality to shine through every object in your home. This is your safe space; your place to retreat to when the day ends. You want to feel safe, seen, and held from the moment you walk in the door.

Step Five: Find Magic in the Mundane

Our minds are powerful things. They can help or hinder us. Our thoughts can either enrich our experiences or trap us within limiting, self-sabotaging beliefs.

We have all heard stories of people who have suffered tragic life events and used the power of their minds to lift themselves up. Likewise, we probably all know that one person who, no matter what opportunities come their way, always focus on the negatives.

We can use our thoughts to create what we want to see in the world, and to help us feel wonder, joy and connection. The law of attraction (LOA) is a popular concept that is based on the idea that like attracts like – that positive thoughts of love, abundance, and vitality, will call in love, abundance and vitality. On the flip side, negative thoughts will call in more negative experiences. In essence, your positive or negative expectations will cause life to present that very experience to you.

Although I do believe that we attract in energies we actively cultivate, the LOA that is talked about in today's society is actually quite problematic, often toxic and steeped in privilege.

Typically, LOA maintains that you are responsible for your current reality. Every negative and positive experience belongs to you, because you called it in with your thought patterns. If you want to experience a better reality, then you need to clean up your thoughts to attract what you wish to see in the world. This is relevant and true, to an extent.

To follow this thought process fully would mean that people are abused because they call it in, people die of cancer because they call it in, and children suffer horrific situations because they call it in. No one deserves any of that, no matter *what*.

It's not someone's mindset that calls in abuse or a painful illness. The cause is either other human beings inflicting pain, genetics, or just luck of the draw. Life has its own agenda and, frankly, sometimes it sucks.

People also have to be experiencing a certain amount of privilege in order to work on mindset. For example, you're less likely to give a crap about thinking positively and manifesting when you're struggling to survive. It is never okay to imply blame, gaslight or shove toxic positivity down someone's throat when they have been a victim to experiences that we can hardly comprehend. We don't get to invalidate another person's story or experience.

That said, I do believe that we can exercise a certain amount of influence over our lives by cultivating a positive mindset. If we are ill and still try to find joy and love in our life, then we are simply going to feel better than someone who is ill and stuck in a cycle of negative thinking. The hard and traumatic times in our lives often (but not always) give us profound understanding, skills and lessons that we may never have learnt otherwise. When I discuss LOA, please know I am not suggesting you are responsible for the cruelty the world may have inflicted upon you. I am suggesting that you have the ability to empower yourself through your mindset and can draw more positive experiences towards you.

We also have the power to attract certain energies and experiences when we focus on them. For example, it's one of those mornings where everything seems to go wrong – you wake up late and stub your toe, becoming so frustrated and flustered that you drink your coffee while it's too hot and burn your tongue. Then you drop your bottle of makeup in your rush to get ready, struggle to find your keys, and get stuck in traffic on the way to work. Now you're late and have to face the wrath of your boss. In this situation, the energy of frustration snowballs and picks up speed, turning everything upside down until we get a moment to breathe, centre and realign our energy.

Vision Boards

Vision boards are a great way to invite the vibes you want into your life and are a direct expression of your creative soul's yearnings to the universe. You can make them as large or small as you like, placing one or many around your home.

Place pictures in a visually pleasing way on your medium so they form a mood board of what you would like to welcome into your life. They could be representations of career, travel, wealth, material items, love or family goals. Don't be shy with your imaginings. As you create your vision board, play music that helps you get into the vibe. Make it a passionate experience so that you infuse the entire process with your wishes and intentions.

Once completed, place or hang the vision board somewhere you will see every day. This way, you will perpetually receive that visual cue, even if you're not spending time consciously looking at it. You could also create digital vision boards and use them as wallpapers on your phone or laptop.

Step Six: Love Yourself

Our opinions on ourselves are often tangled up with feelings of self-loathing, inadequacy, comparison and rejection, all mixed in with an unhealthy amount of other people's opinions.

We look to others to fill in the holes and flaws we think we have; to make us whole. It's not our fault. For our entire lives we are fed the myth that the perfect someone to complete us is out there. This idea is reinforced over and over again, through stories and movies.

The truth is that we are whole and perfect, just as we are. We are our own soulmates. All we need to do is wake up to this truth and start the journey back home to ourselves.

I want to give you an alternative narrative. We each have a higher self. This higher self is not dependent on or contained within our physical bodies or this physical realm. You can call it your higher self, your soul, your spirit – whatever word works for you.

What if our longing for a soulmate, a partner that will complete us and make us feel whole, is actually a longing to complete ourselves, because deep down we know there is a part missing? We aren't searching for another person (as we have been taught), but are longing for a full-bodied connection to *all* parts of ourselves – our physical, shadow, and higher selves.

All through my life, I was dependent on others. I depended on friends, family, and my ex-husband to validate me and provide direction. I became caught up in trying to be the perfect daughter, then the perfect partner, wife and mother. I started to value others' opinions over mine and slowly eroded my sense of self. I wasn't a mindless puppet by any stretch, but I wasn't a well-rounded, whole one either.

After my marriage broke up, I found myself living entirely on my own terms for the first time in my life. I raised my children by myself, decorated my house how I wanted, and made decisions without anyone else weighing in or offering direction. It was both liberating and hugely terrifying. Every single decision (or indecision) was on me, and often I was paralysed with fear that I would get it wrong. Then it dawned on me: there is no wrong, only experiences and lessons learned. If I wanted to trust myself, I had to get to know myself. When I got to know myself, I learned to truly love myself. It didn't matter if I was surrounded by people or completely alone, the one constant was *me* and that was the relationship I had to prioritise.

In order for us to become fully autonomous individuals, we have to explore every facet of our personalities. We have to dive into self-love. We have to learn our strengths, weaknesses, and shadows. As we wade through the muck, we learn how to love ourselves in our wholeness.

In finding true love and reverence for ourselves, we cannot turn away or deny the spark of divinity in another. If we honour and cherish our unique traits, we will love and defend another's right to express their unique traits and quirks too. This is how we can reach wholeness as individuals and as a community.

Mirror Work

Set a comfy chair in front of a mirror and make yourself a hot drink. A box of tissues and a journal to write your insights in may also be good to have nearby. Sit down and spend a few moments looking into your eyes in the mirror. (This in itself can feel awkward and confronting.) Stop and say some affirmations, or just sit gazing into your eyes.

When you are ready, have a chat with yourself, just like you would with a close friend. Talk out all the problems you are having. Be open and honest. Vent your frustrations and voice your inner critic. This critic is the voice that tells you that you aren't good enough or loveable, and questions who you are to chase your dreams or show up the way you want in the world.

During this practice, the most important thing is to maintain eye contact the whole time. Focus on the light shining out of your eyes (this is especially important as you say anything mean or critical).

As you look into your eyes, I want you to imagine your reflection is the face of a treasured friend, family member, or your own child. Would you ever say these disparaging, critical things to them? Would you be able to watch the light in their eyes dim, the sparkle disappear and the tears well up as you unleash your harsh words? I'm guessing you wouldn't. So why, my love, are you talking this way to yourself?

Give yourself time to process the emotions that are coming up. Be gentle with yourself. As you maintain eye contact, I want you to list all the ways you matter, and all the wonderful qualities that only you possess. Tell yourself you are forgiven for being overly critical, for past mistakes, for whatever is coming up for you.

When I did this mirror exercise for the first time after my divorce, I cried so much my head hurt. I looked into my eyes and as I gave voice to my inner critic, I imagined they were the eyes of my daughters or sons. My heart broke at the thought of my children thinking they were anything less than phenomenal. Then my heart broke for myself, because I deserved that same fierce love that I had been denying myself for decades.

I've done it several times since, and each time I feel another layer of self-loathing and self-criticism dissolve. Take it slow with this exercise and be willing to lean into the uncomfortable; our shadow self and pain have so much wisdom to teach us. These aspects of ourselves are not the enemies, they are just our wounded teachers. If we show them compassion and acknowledge their presence within us, they will unlock a deeper level of wisdom, understanding and peace.

FEELING WHOLE AGAIN

It might sound crazy, but I wouldn't change a thing about what happened in my marriage breakdown. It was horrific, but was exactly what I needed, because without it I never would have left. I would have continued to give parts of myself away, twisting myself into what I thought I needed to be in order to be the perfect wife and mother, whilst missing the mark every time.

The simple truth was, I left myself a long time before my husband left me. I stopped having my own life and investing in my own happiness. Instead, I gave that power over to someone else entirely.

Through my journey to heal, I have discovered who I truly am. It wasn't always easy. (In fact, when you work on yourself and commit to healing, learning, growing, taking radical self-responsibility, and showing up for yourself consistently, it is inevitable that you will encounter bumps along the way.)

Practise what resonates with you. Put in the effort and lean in with love. Celebrate the beautiful moments and seek out the wonder and the humour that is available to you. When you walk this path, your journey will inevitably lead you to remember the truth we are all born with, but easily forget: all the magic you ever needed was inside you, all along.

TAKE HEART, TAKE HOLD

A father's fight to cure his son's epilepsy

MARK COLLINS

MARK COLLINS

From doting dad to determined humanitarian, Mark Collins has leveraged his challenges into philanthropic success. Founder of YOUschool, a learning organisation with the purpose of helping young people choose their best path in life, it is Mark's lived experiences that help him give children the best opportunities to enjoy happy, loving, and joyful lives through to adulthood.

It is from his son, Max, that Mark draws inspiration. After being diagnosed with epilepsy at age five, Max has spent the years since in and out of hospitals – his dad by his side every step of the way. Mark has spent this time learning everything he can about his son's condition, raising money, and promoting awareness for epilepsy.

It was his son's illness that spurred Mark to focus on his own health and wellbeing, recognising the direct effect and influence that the energy of others had on his son's symptoms. Having endured his own health struggles after being diagnosed with testicular cancer at just 27 years old, Mark had already experienced the benefits of mindful living when it came to his health. However, it wasn't until Mark saw the connection between his own and his son's wellbeing, that he focused more heavily on self-care practises.

Mark began regularly practising meditation, yoga and eating natural foods with Max as a way of assisting him in his treatment. Mark sees the benefits of alternative medicine and is a champion for holistic healing. With his partner Sansan, Mark continues to learn about using the mind and body to overcome all sorts of challenges. Together, they help relieve the problems of others.

You can connect with Mark at mark.collo1404@gmail.com and on 04 1903 6137.

I lost count of the tally of seizures; sometimes over fifty in a single day. My son's young body would drop to the ground without warning, convulsing and shuddering in rigid, jerking movements while I would jump into action, placing pillows around him and holding his head, offering some protection as his body contorted without control. It never got easier seeing his eyes roll back in their sockets and his sweet smiling face tighten in the spasm's grasp.

Sadly, I knew the drill too well. My son Max had been diagnosed with epilepsy at age five and since then I have been continually searching for the right treatment for him. I have been on a mission to give our son a normal life; a healthy and happy life. Unfortunately, this simple birthright has been thwarted by chronic seizures that strike on their own terms, without warning.

GIVING UP IS NOT AN OPTION

My name is Mark. I am a father of three beautiful children. I'm a regular guy who has gone down some irregular paths to give his extraordinary son every chance at a regular life – how miraculous regular would be.

Over the years I have seen countless neurologists, tried multiple medications and consulted numerous experts hoping someone could shed light on my son's condition. His medication has been lowered, raised and even trialled, all with no sign of change. Brain scans, blood tests, monitoring and medical treatment have all come to a dead-end with no positive outcomes. It has been frustrating and depressing to say the least.

There is so much damage the doctors don't see: my son's social restrictions, constant supervision, no competitive sports, interrupted sleep patterns, constant doctors' appointments, far-off specialist appointments, frequent school absences, simple daily activities interrupted by small seizures, no sleepovers with friends, living with a seizure monitor under his mattress, speech impediments, learning difficulties and frequent blood tests, all of these burdens have become his form of 'regular'.

After years and years of frustration and torment, a parent can only take so much. I couldn't sit back and watch him battle these adversities without hope for change. I decided that if conventional medicine didn't have the answers, then I would explore all other options; leaving no stone unturned.

MAX

Max was first diagnosed in his first year at school. I had already noticed how Max would sometimes zone out with a blank stare, unable to hear me. His preschool teacher had noticed it too, along with his speech falling behind. They were brief, minor episodes but looking back they were the start of it.

I learnt they were called absence seizures and I was somewhat prepared when Max was properly diagnosed. By the end of that first year at school, Max was experiencing myoclonic seizures, or complex partial absence seizures, with jerking movements and loss of awareness. Max was prescribed medication that initially I was hopeful about however his battle continued unabated, leading to his first tonic clonic seizure in 2018.

It struck two months after the passing of his grandmother whom he loved very much. I was at home with Max and my eldest daughter at the time. We were having a casual dinner in the lounge room, just talking, taking it easy. Max was standing up and he began to slowly spin around, looking up at something on the ceiling it seemed.

"Max, what are you doing?" I asked playfully.

In response he simply toppled backwards onto his plate of food and jerked into unconsciousness. Even though I was familiar with epilepsy by that point, this moment was a huge shock. In the back of my mind I knew it had been a possibility but I confess I just panicked. To see your child suddenly collapse beneath a force so powerful and out of anyone's control is heart-wrenching.

Four different neurologists have failed to explain why it happens or to find a treatment that works for him. I have been frustrated beyond belief with the fact that the only change these doctors make is in the dose of medication; medication that has shown no signs of actually making a difference.

I understand epilepsy is not an easy disorder to treat and every experienced doctor will say each case is different. Maybe I expected that to mean, "If we don't find the right treatment through regular avenues, we won't stop until we do."

It has not been that way.

I mechanically followed the conventional path without question: son has a suspected brain issue – take him to GP – GP refers to paediatrician – paediatrician refers to neurologist – neurologist prescribes anticonvulsant tablets and a label for my son.

Despite my blind commitment to this process, the years rolled by and I found myself powerless as Max fell more and more behind in so many developmental areas. Not to mention the toll all these non-happenings, rules, regulations, red-tape and dashed hopes were having on Max internally, trampling on his precious childhood years.

By July 2019, I was left thinking, *Now what?* What happens when the professionals cannot bring a result or a change? Who can I turn to?

I felt backed into an impossible corner and after the worst year of my life worrying about my whole family and their health and happiness, I realised I could no longer sit around waiting for a white knight, waiting for a miracle.

I chose to become the miracle.

Like a puzzle falling into place, I thought about how much time I spent with Max every day, helping him to read, to write, to remember things, riding in the ambulance with him, sitting in waiting rooms, watching seizure after seizure, often losing count, so much time spent noticing patterns and triggers.

I thought back on how I had researched epilepsy, raised money for epilepsy and explored alternative treatments. I didn't have a certificate proving what I knew, but I did have an intimate and practical understanding of Max's challenges. I took too long to realise the only person I had not trusted with my son's condition was me.

MISSION LAUNCHED

I embraced my mission to learn as much as I could, in my own way, about the human brain, body and its behaviours. I realised that only focusing on the western philosophy of anatomy and medicine had been limiting my options, Max's options. There was a wealth of cultural and ancient wisdom to be discovered about health and healing that I hadn't given a chance yet. I needed a more holistic approach.

My initial research led me to firstly take stock of our family's unique situation. Our household had been under unusual stress for many years, and naturally there were often many emotions flying around with five people living in the house. I contributed significantly to the level of peace or otherwise in the house at any one time. I discovered how my own perspective and behaviours affect those around me.

Perspectives and behaviours that often stem back to the conditioning of our youth. Thankfully, there was a mountain of information to draw upon about retraining our brains from these limiting beliefs. I became more aware of my thoughts, focusing on positivity and not letting the same patterns take hold as they had done for so many years. I wanted to break out of that cycle.

I started with something not too 'out there': meditation. This is when my path as a 'regular' bloke probably first diverged because it was incredible, illuminating even. I began incorporating meditation at the end of my day with the purpose of finding peace and synchronicity from within, instead of looking for those sensations to be given to me from an outside source.

Meditation came surprisingly naturally to me; it felt both fascinating and familiar. When I was very young and found myself feeling unwell or perhaps with a headache, instead of running to my parents looking for a headache tablet, I used to try to fix it myself from within. Going into hibernation mode I'd block everything else out and concentrate on feeling good in order to get out of the state I was in. And I remember many times it worked.

This was a kind of intuitive meditation that was gradually stifled by western cultural pragmatism as I entered adolescence and then the rigid dogma of adulthood. I had been living for so long under the weight of those systems, how would I break free?

I considered a more recent and profound experience I had in 2009. I had been diagnosed with testicular cancer and there was a week of not knowing whether or not it had spread. During that week my lower back, hips and legs were in so much pain I couldn't even stand up sometimes, let alone work.

Once the news came through that the cancer had not spread, instantly the pain stopped. I had been in such a heightened state of stress, worry and anxiety that my thoughts had been triggering the significant pain I was feeling. As soon as the stress, worry and anxiety were alleviated, so was the pain.

This memory had planted the seed about the power of the mind (call it placebo if you prefer). It created a much more critical eye for me to question medication and pain tablets and explore using my mind for relief instead, much more than is considered in the realms of convention.

It inspired me to keep a record of my experiments as I learned, all in the name of finding relief for my young son. It was not enough for me to simply go through the motions; I would be my own test cast.

I listed my physical and mental issues that needed to be fixed. I regularly experienced aches and pains associated with my knee reconstruction and other old injuries, numbness leftover from chemotherapy, a fear of many things such as love, finance and health, as well as depression and anxiety. Conventionally these ailments would all be treated separately were I to go to a medical clinic. My hope was to show that these conditions could be treated all together in the mind itself.

I learnt to track my awareness through my body during meditation. The principle being where you place your attention, your energy will follow. When this happens, beginning from the perineum to above the head and all the way through, it is slowly bringing your body closer to its natural coherence. When your inner world is in coherence, your outer world will reflect that and you will get back what you are broadcasting energetically. These are concepts embodied by many ancient and modern cultures around the world.

During meditation I could physically feel the pulsing of my body wherever I moved my focus. After only two weeks of meditation and staying aware of my thoughts throughout the day I noticed the following:

1. I was being friendlier.

2. I was smiling more often, sometimes for no reason.

3. People seemed to want to talk to me.

4. Those closest to me were happier, even if it was just a minor change.

5. Almost no pain in my left foot that had been suffering plantar fasciitis.

6. I could feel my fingertips – a ten-year first since chemotherapy.

7. I had absolutely no lower back or hip pain.

8. My right knee was pain free and I had no cramping in my hamstring.

9. I procrastinated less at work.

10. I felt more energetic.

11. My thoughts were more positive and clear.

12. I believed whatever thoughts and energy I put out into the universe would come back to me in similar ways.

I was convinced that I was achieving my goal of healing my physical symptoms. This was a momentous time for me because from that point I sensed the interconnection between emotion and energy that physically affects the body.

Positive emotion creates high frequencies of flowing energy and negative emotions create low, heavy vibrations that cause blockages in the internal flow, physically and mentally. I didn't know it at the time, but this would prove a key factor to discover in Max's journey.

SMALL *REAL* STEPS

I was pumped up with my success so I was keen to start the next experiment; *could I raise my emotional capacity and energy to a point where I could change the lives of my family members for the better?*

Within days I clearly noticed that when I practiced positivity and gratitude, my children picked up on these behaviours and replicated them. When I showed energy and good health, they showed it too. Most interesting of all, I realised when I spent the majority of the day with my son; his seizure activity would be lower than usual, to the point where his daily seizures were in single digits rather than in the thirties or more.

Another sign occurred a few weeks later when Max and I were getting ready for two days of specialist appointments, which included significant travel. The anxiety involved in anticipating these trips usually sparked a bad day with countless seizures. This time, I was actively feeling and thinking positive and calming thoughts and Max sensed these 'signals' and he only had five seizures that day.

In October 2019 Max and I flew to Sydney for a 'regular' neurologist appointment, that turned into a journey of life-changing synchronicity for Max. We had some time to waste before the appointment and were relaxing in the Coogee Beach area. I was scrolling through social media and saw a post in a private group I had joined recently through meditation. Another member of the group mentioned Coogee Beach and I posted a reply, as I happened to be there at that moment.

After some basic chat I found out that she was a health and wellness practitioner and was interested in my son's condition. She knew of another woman nearby who she thought would be perfect to treat Max although she acknowledged she didn't take new clients, never had cancellations and she knew we were on very limited time anyway.

That could have easily been the end of it; however within the hour this practitioner had five unheard of cancellations and was able to see us before we flew home. I can't emphasise enough how amazing this encounter was. Max made significant steps towards healing after this encounter.

This practitioner was an experienced chiropractor, kinesiologist, neuroscientist and pharmacologist and had had success with epilepsy sufferers in the past. She performed cranial-sacral adjustments on Max, some through the roof of his mouth, and achieved more results in twenty-five minutes than anyone else had in seven years! She taught me about retained neonatal reflexes and the fact that Max experienced an emergency extraction with forceps a week overdue is likely to have had a significant influence on his condition.

A lot of serendipitous events conspired in our favour that day. Ever since opening my heart and eyes to the energy running through everything, this sort of positive outcome was becoming more frequent in general. For example, it was around this time that I finally found a doctor willing to prescribe cannabis oil (CBD) to my son to treat his epilepsy.

My pursuit of CBD oil had been a long and arduous journey of red-tape, swings and roundabouts. At one point in 2018, Max was actually accepted into a clinical trial for a synthetically developed version of CBD gel. The first month saw great results and I thought it was the answer we had been looking for.

However, Max's emotions were dealt a massive blow during this trial. His grandmother was diagnosed terminally ill with cancer and passed away within two months. Max's loss and confusion were compounded by the significant grief we experienced and also by the fact that everyone he was close to was living in the fight-or-flight stress mode themselves.

Surrounded by such negative, heavy energy Max fell back into the same patterns of countless small myoclonic seizures every day, up to 50; he was far worse than he had ever been, finally culminating in his first full tonic clonic seizure two months after the funeral. Apart from Max's emotional trauma, the trial displayed a lot of potential for CBD oil but was once again out of reach once the trial ended.

Upon returning from our positive trip to Sydney, I was contacted by a journalist regarding the difficulty in accessing CBD. After their article was published in the local paper, I was contacted by some sympathetic people who put me in touch with a doctor willing to prescribe CBD oil for unique cases. This doctor's practice also included kinesiology and reiki as care options for their patients; a much more holistic approach.

I was feeling optimistic until the doctor explained I would need a letter of referral from Max's neurologist to go with the government application that was necessary for the prescription.

Immediately I thought, *That will be a struggle.*

I understand now that creating that thought and letting it out into the universe had a hand in what I received back. The neurologist would not provide the referral. Her reason was that she had not heard of the brand the doctor wanted to prescribe. I persisted and asked, "What is the difference between this brand and the brand you know but won't prescribe Max yourself?"

It's not worth the space to articulate the roundabout discussion that ensued. What she did not say was much clearer; I believe the brand in question would not benefit her people financially and it would not look good for her to be supporting a different product.

I say this because this neurologist was part of the team conducting the trial of the synthetically made CBD gel that Max had participated in the year before. That lab-made medication had been untried and its long-term effects unknown, and yet the doctor had deemed it safe enough for my son to use.

Now she was saying natural CBD, marketed by a different company than the synthetic version, was not suitable to use; different companies equalled no financial incentives. Max's conventional medication, which he's been on for many years, lists hundreds of potential short-term side effects and can only hint at how many *unknown* long-term ones there are. If you ask me, hypocrisy and double standards reigned.

Experiences like this, and there have been too many to recount here, have demonstrated repeatedly that in the eyes of many western medical practices, Max is a paying customer first and a patient second. If everyone were to suddenly cure themselves, a huge industry would suddenly lose a lot of money on a global scale.

This is why there is such a subliminal focus on the stresses of life by clever marketing, the media and big industry. Big players design it this way so that the unsuspecting general public are convinced they need to be prescribed a magic pill to make them feel better. My experiences have confirmed that this system is designed to fail but with just enough upside to it, to keep us in the cycle, keeping our dollars rolling in.

Now I am mindful of the power of excessively pursuing such negative associations, so I will lastly acknowledge that while these experiences left me disillusioned in many ways, ultimately they provided the incredible opportunities to discover the interplay between emotion and energy. This opened the door to understanding the principle of natural cohesion and the blockages Max was experiencing.

THE LESSONS CONTINUE

In November 2019 however, this was all still a work in progress. I had been back from Sydney for a few months and was navigating a path somewhere between conventional medicine and the groundbreaking principles I had connected with.

For many years Max had persistently displayed cold-like symptoms and he was eventually referred to an ear, nose and throat specialist who recommended a tonsillectomy. The nerves and anxiety leading up to such a surgery would normally trigger countless seizures. However, since the cranial adjustments in Sydney, Max had been going incredibly well.

I had not been totally convinced of the need for the tonsillectomy, however I let myself be guided by more conventional expectations (that I still wrestled with) and went ahead with the procedure. Max is the most amazing trooper, happy to experience any discomfort or unknown procedure in the hope that it will give him a chance at a more regular childhood.

There was no immediate improvement following the surgery. In fact, I believe much of the progress he had made following the cranial adjustment in Sydney, was undermined due to the prolonged position of Max's head and jaw during surgery.

However, an important breakthrough came about shortly after the surgery. I had taken Max to see a nutritionist who recommended removing hard to digest foods from his diet; these can fill the blood with toxins through the gut lining. Removing wheat, dairy, corn and soy from our daily intake (I wasn't going to ask him to do it alone, so I joined him) was transforming.

His usually red, spotty, lumpy skin smoothed out, his cold-like symptoms were alleviated dramatically, and I felt amazing too. This was another mind-blowing experience proving nature and our own bodies know better.

The nutritionist mentioned that she knew of five other recent cases of the same surgery that had done nothing to help the patient's symptoms. I likened it to a warning light coming on in your car. Do you remove the light and assume the problem is fixed? The body has warning lights too, such as the tonsils. They often get blamed for a lot, but they are not creating illness. They are simply showing signs of a deeper problem.

The change in his diet was responsible for the positive effect and Max now takes supplements to strengthen the gut lining and help the liver kick the toxins from the body. This is another one of the many positive *self-made* changes that has actually made a difference in Max's life.

Every little step is exciting because we never know which one will finally tip the scales so we can reach our target of consistently zero seizures in a day for Max. We are down to single digits, but I won't stop until he reaches maximum potential. Max has come so far when I think back to July 2019 when he was experiencing countless seizures each day and I was at an utter loss as to whom I could turn to.

Another typically futile appointment to one of Max's specialists was coming up and I had decided to turn it into a family trip to the city staying in a hotel. Just days before we were due to depart, I was shocked to receive a letter from the hotel stating they were unable to keep the booking due to the supposed risks associated with Max's condition. I was completely stunned and dismayed at such hurtful, misguided discrimination. When I vented my outrage on social media, the story went national. I was flooded with positive comments, acts of kindness and offers to help from strangers.

However, once the comments died down and the media attention went away, I was left with a void. I felt I had talked the talk but not walked the walk. I wasn't convinced the public perception of me as a fantastic father who gives his son every chance to heal and live a normal life, was completely justified.

I had to admit to myself that I was not doing anywhere near as much as I could for my son. I was passively hoping, wishing, wanting something to jump out of the blue and fix him. This attention and subsequent realisation helped me align my vision with the conviction to be that man they thought I was for my son. The whole incident was the catalyst for genuine change.

Nowadays I know not to be a victim of someone else's behaviour and would no longer 'react' like this internally or play it out on social media. But in this case, I took it as a sign pointing me in the right direction.

WE ALL NEED SUPPORT

In early 2020, I created a support group for fathers like me, 'Fathers Of Special Needs Kids'. It's a private group run through social media where fathers can share their feelings, good or otherwise, in an understanding and supportive environment. I had seen a real need for such a group, and within weeks the benefit of listening and helping each other through tough times became clear as dads commented how much it helped them.

It's been a particularly worthy and successful undertaking; it's no secret men generally have a hard time opening up about what is affecting them. I believe it's time to blast that characteristic back to the past. It's an old way of thinking, generationally passed down, that men shouldn't show their emotions, that it's weak, that big boys don't cry – you know the drill.

But if we look at it objectively, if you bottle your emotions up as a father, what will your child learn to do? If you don't process your emotions as they arise, don't acknowledge and release them, what will your child learn to do?

This community of men is there to serve the emotional needs of fathers who have the perceived added stress of having a struggling child. Encouraging the natural processing of emotion for fathers will enable the same effect in their child. If you're stressed, stuck, worried, frustrated or angry, you are only going to make yourself ill. If you don't take a step to deal with what you feel as a father and man, you are telling your child; I'm not worthy.

Children learn by what they see. You can tell them it's good to talk about and process your feelings, but if they don't *see* you do it yourself, they will not do it either. If you are showing them you aren't worthy of feeling better, that's exactly what they will believe of themselves.

I have had to put myself in perceived vulnerable positions regularly to keep making tough progress. I identified that my beliefs and barriers had to be removed so that my son could flourish. I had to realise that I was not doing things in his best interest as I thought I was. My behaviours and thoughts were still feeding my old beliefs and affecting those around me. I would raise my voice, grunt, sulk and even swear. All of this stuff I either did in full view of or even at my kids. This is the truth I have confronted.

I was also addicted to the praise of others, telling me what a courageous dad I was, how inspirational I was perceived to be, for what I did for my son. Or I would try out some self pity, telling people how hard it was, travelling here and there for appointments, not a lot of time for much else, blah blah. I was feeding my own needs and wasting time indulging in how it made me feel. None of it was helpful to myself or to my son, rather it was taking an enormous toll on us both.

Guess what was happening? All of this time and energy spent producing the negative thoughts, emotions and words only ensured that I would continue to receive exactly those things in return. The cycle continued until I consciously took my first step away from it and onto this path. Outwardly this journey has been for my son, but totally unexpected has been my own exponential personal growth.

Each day I am building my knowledge of how to train our own energy. I now believe without question that the 3 Ms – **movement, mindfulness** and **meditation** – can be used to overcome the 3 Ts – **trauma, toxins** and (negative) **thoughts**. My ambition is to see this message commonly taught to everyone from a young age.

PERCEPTION IS KEY

Instead of perceiving life from a place of doubt and powerlessness, I want to share the knowledge of how I have learnt no one thing is good or bad, it is our perception that creates the feeling. For example, when we moved house to a better living space (as we perceived it to be), one that suited our needs, our energies rose as the house was new to us and we perceived the new house gave us the positive feeling. For a time, we felt happier because of it.

After a while the experience of the 'new' house became normal and our energies lowered. The outside source (new house) that we attributed to the original rise in energy had no real influence over anything. It was our emotions being influenced by our perception of external events over time. We have the power over our perception. If we didn't, we would forever rely on 'new houses' to make us happy, how futile.

Now I set out each day with the intention of creating my own peace and energy from within that exudes outwards onto others; quite the opposite of what we were raised to do conventionally speaking. I begin inwards through meditation, connecting with body and nature that produces calmness and courage to embrace whatever unfolds each day.

It is not for me to make my son do these things in his day too. He naturally wants to do what he likes, not what his father wants him to do. It is for me however, to do these things myself so that his developing mind creates mirror neurons that take on as much of what he sees and feels from my behaviour as possible.

Now, he naturally joins me in yoga every morning, he gets outside more and he shows more gratitude. Just as I have learnt to take on challenges with vigour and excitement, now he does too.

I was so excited to witness how much Max's cognitive function had improved at the start of the new school year when he entered Year 6. He showed few signs of the stress, anxiety and nervousness he once had. His trunk was more solid, and his face looked so much more relaxed, like his body was doing less fighting. A lot of it was also because of his change in diet; his body could simply make the most of the natural foods he was eating.

I know our new behaviours and perceptions are working when I see the effects of a dip in consistency. During one particular week I didn't do my normal morning yoga, had too many late nights and not enough sleep and meditation; it was the same for Max. After a second day of bad seizure activity he said to me without prompting, "Dad, I think it's because I haven't been doing yoga."

We got straight back into our routine once again.

When I weighed up all the facets of how Max perceives his reality, I realised it was vital to understand how our perception is created and influenced:

• Our biological cells are a creation of a signal binding with a protein. The signal is your consciousness; the type of signal (good or bad) is your perception. The cell's reaction is determined by the signal.

• Genetics are just a blueprint, they have no control at all.

• The way our genes are expressed is dependent on the cell receptor that reads the signal which is influenced by changes (perceived and real) in its external environment.

• Stress produces the chemical cortisol, which in large amounts, switches off the immune system.

• The modern lifestyle is purposefully designed to be artificially stressful and is full of toxins and trauma.

It is that last statement that has become my mission to minimise in Max's life. No one has ever found a physical reason for my son's condition. The only logical supposition left is that the signal his cells are receiving is bad, meaning his energy and what directs his energy (thoughts, perception, stress and anxiety) is the root cause.

Each family has their own set of generational baggage and ours is no different. I believe a lot of past and unresolved trauma and energy was unwittingly imprinted onto Max's gene expression from when he was conceived in fact. His unique biology and set of influencers created his physical manifestations.

To give you a simple insight, one night at home in early 2020 Max experienced a cluster of myoclonic seizures that lasted around ten minutes with only a few seconds in between. Instead of panicking and dragging the energy down, I calmly sat and asked him questions every chance I could. I sensed he was anxious about something.

Finally, I hit the right question, "What do you want for dinner?" It took another moment in between seizures for him to answer, "Sausages," to which I again had to wait for another moment in between to let him know that that was okay, we could have sausages.

The absolute second that he processed the answer the cluster stopped completely, leaving me in no doubt that it is an energy issue not a physical one. If Max was feeling anxious about what he was having for dinner, you can imagine the step up in effect for each element he has to cope within his day.

Another instance occurred when his school support officer called to say they were worried about the amount of myoclonic or absence seizures Max was having that day (anything out of the ordinary was their cue to call us). I drove to pick him up and noticed he was looking a little pale and tired.

The teacher looked worried and said, "I'm sorry we just can't do any work today, there's just too much activity going on." I smiled at her and said it's not a reason to stress. She was perplexed.

To Max I said playfully, "G'day Mate, how's things?" He said hi and then I asked him what was on his mind.

"I'm just nervous."

"What about?" I asked.

He told me it was his upcoming specialist appointment and school projects. As soon as he revealed his feeling of nervousness, his whole energy changed. There was no sign of the seizure activity that had been plaguing his day.

The act of trying to contain his nervousness was triggering multiple seizures. As soon as he decided he was comfortable telling me he was nervous, the tension in his body abated, which led to a more comfortable, natural flow of energy.

The two school officers watching on were amazed at the transformation, like I had made something magically disappear. "Incredible transformation," they said with disbelief. I still took him home for the rest of the day, to let his body recover after fighting itself all morning.

Numerous moments like this keep validating me that my son's problem was emotional. He has simultaneously struggled with fear of the unknown, anxiety, guilt, self-doubt, stress, sadness and grief. Negative emotion is the number one cause of disease and illness. There is a blockage of energy somewhere that prevents my son from processing emotions regularly. Being ultra-sensitive to toxins of all kinds is also a valid reason, however it is a secondary indicator that his energy is stuck somewhere.

Many of his triggers are out of my control, and that's life. But so much is also within my control, once I show him the way. He now has a basic understanding of the power of the unseen and the importance of high frequency energy simply explained to him as love, gratitude and joy. My daughters also understand how finding joy and fun in everything makes their life so much better.

From those experiments I started in July 2019, where I practised self-healing through meditation and energy focus, I have not had one health issue to speak of, not one! I never took medication for them, had no other treatments for them and the only difference was in the mind itself.

Well before starting this journey officially, I think my repressed beliefs from childhood made me predisposed for this kind of path. Reaching my lowest point of despair for Max triggered a primal response to our circumstances and I see everything that has happened to this point has been *on the way*, not *in the way*.

These discoveries also reminded me that I have always been sceptical of the perceived authorities in life. Not to say I disobeyed laws or deliberately broke fundamental rules. I simply did not like being told what to do without good reason.

Even at school, I often challenged the teachers' rhetoric when they couldn't justify why things were done a certain way. Through tertiary education and trade schools, I was never a favourite student because I had a need to question everything and felt a lack of incentive to do things the 'right' way.

I am the one who, instead of blindly believing the next new thing to fear (as told to us by the media), I take issue with the rampant panic and stupidity it evokes. Fearmongering and the subliminal marketing we are exposed to adds immensely to our stress levels, making us susceptible to illness. So, we take ourselves off to the doctor for a pill – how convenient for them!

This has been such a revolutionary cycle for me to understand and recognise our roles in. I am convinced that had I not started looking at Max's situation from a different perspective, we would still be on the merry-go-round, frustrated by the conventional system that doesn't actually know how to help him.

I would also still be convincing myself I am doing the best I can, waiting for a fix to just happen, wondering why all this stuff happens to me, while at the same time feeding my need for validation and attention. I would still be lost in myself and my own problems, which was creating half the issue for Max.

LIGHTNESS

In March 2020, our state legislature finally caught up to the 21st century and CBD oil for medicinal purposes was categorised by the government as a category 4, which meant all of the red-tape and extra government applications were no longer needed. Thank you, universe!

While no financial barrier will stop me from doing what I need to do for my son, I concede the cost is a little steep at around $200 for 25ml of Max's particular prescription. However, the universe again came to our aid in the form of the most generous local business people who chose to help my family out by way of a giant raffle in support of my son's appointments and treatments. My whole family is forever grateful for the efforts of our caring and generous hometown, thank you!

Every day at the dinner table my son asks us all what our favourite part of the day was. It is a constant reminder of the genuine love and care that is naturally within my son (and all children in fact). We don't need to teach them to love. We just need to *not* teach them how to hate, how to be angry, how to be jealous, how to resent.

Self-care is an important lesson we can teach them, this includes encouraging their own identity without the influence of our own perceived hurts or society's expectations. Many children get left behind in the current education system because they don't fit the structure and these kids internalise and suffer in unique ways because of it. After everything I had learnt from this very irregular yet successful path for Max, I asked myself, could I share this philosophy to help other kids?

The answer came to me as YOUschool; a learning space I have created where kids are encouraged to shed the weight of expectation, social beliefs, generational behaviour and other limiting factors and shine their own beautiful light. The program's aim is to help young people give themselves every opportunity to live happy, loving and positive lives by identifying their own truths and values and empowering them to live them. Not everyone is ready for it just because I am. But I want to be there when they are.

I send my endless gratitude to the many insightful people who taught me so much on this journey, most of all to my brave and determined son, Max. He is my motivator and my grounding, all in one; a magical soul who never fails to make me smile, as do my kind, spirited daughters. I am blessed to have such loving souls in my life as my support and inspiration.

We have recently returned from Max's second cranial treatment session in Sydney and his general wellbeing is the best it's ever been. He has so much more energy, leaping ahead in his speech. He is brighter during the day, sleeping better at night, and I love how inquisitive he has become about everything. Remember the joy and adventure of exploring as a child? Max has finally been given this exquisite gift.

His future has begun.

We are sharing more in the INTERACTIVE book.

See exclusive downloads, videos, audios and photos.

DOWNLOAD it for free at deanpublishing.com/yshift/thriving

"THE SECRET OF
GOOD HEALTH LIES
IN SUCCESSFUL
ADJUSTMENT
TO CHANGING
STRESSES ON
THE BODY."

– HARRY J. JOHNSON –

EVERY SLICE
OF THE PIE

JULIDE TURKER

Y SHIFT

JULIDE TURKER

If you were to ask Julide Turker to sum up her number one principle when it comes to health, it would be 'prevention is better than cure'.

Julide believes that the more work you do in setting the foundations of optimum mental, physical and spiritual wellness, the less you will have to do further down the track. It is her focus on assisting clients implement sustainable lifestyle modifications through nutrition, supplementation, and mindset coaching that helps stave off illness and subdue the effects of the aging process.

Julide employs a holistic approach when it comes to treatment. She considers that the mind, body and spirit are of equal importance when it comes to a person's health, and that a person cannot achieve peak health if they are not well in all of these areas.

Often referred to as 'The Muslim Naturopath', Julide's practice is grounded in prophetic medicine, as she aims to better the health of women and children through conscious living. Julide seeks to serve God by acting as vessel in connecting her clients to their creator.

Julide completed a joint degree in Nutrition and Herbal Medicine at the Australian College of Natural Medicine, and Master's in Food Sciences and Engineering at the University of Melbourne. She currently consults children and women one-on-one in the areas of childhood illness, female reproductive illness, and pre-conceptive and post-conceptive care.

Julide is currently in the process of writing her first book, *One Third of Your Stomach*, to be published by Dean Publishing. In Julide's book, you will discover information and guidance on nutrition, movement, preventative care, spirituality, and mental health, all grounded in holistic and prophetic medicine.

Julide is a proud wife and mother of two young children. She lives in Melbourne, Australia.

You can connect with Julide at www.julideturkernw.com and @julideturkernatropathy on Instagram.

"To ensure good health: eat lightly, breathe deeply, live moderately, cultivate cheerfulness, and maintain an interest in life."
William Londen

Have you heard the parable about the elephant and the blind men?

During the night, an elephant was placed in front of a group of blind men. But, of course, they could not see it. So, one by one, they each reached out, touching the animal to discover what it was.

The first man touched the ears of the elephant. "It is like a huge fan!" he exclaimed.

The second man stroked its back, concluding, "The elephant is like a platform."

"You are all wrong," retorted the third man as he brushed his hand down the animal's leg. "This is like a pillar!"

Finally, it was the last man's turn. He extended his palm, landing on the elephant's trunk. After a few moments, he spoke. "According to me, this elephant is long and hollow within."

Of course, none of the men were correct. Because they were unable to see what was before them, they had drawn conclusions about the elephant, based only off the parts they had physical access to. By focusing on only one portion of the elephant, rather than the whole, their perception and understanding was incomplete.

* * *

In life, we often fall victim to these shortcomings. Like the story of the blind men and the elephant, our assumptions are limited to our own narrow perceptions as we are not able to view the perspective of others. This leaves us failing to see the bigger, complete, picture.

Conventional medicine bears the same shortcoming of linearity. Like the parable of the elephant, we look at one symptom and identify a treatment plan based on it alone, without considering the unity of the rest of the body. Modern medicine assumes that each organ is merely mechanical. If something is diseased – if we can live without it – we cut it out and discard it as a useless piece of flesh. After all, that is exactly what it is now that it is 'not working the way that it should'. Instead of trying to understand why this piece of flesh is no longer functioning optimally by considering the surrounding context, we only treat one part of the 'elephant'. This is a non-holistic approach. For as long as man disconnects the importance of his environment and spiritual self from his physical self, the linear method will never breed health and wellness in its entirety.

This is in direct opposition to the principles of natural medicine.

TAKING THE PATH TO HOLISTIC HEALTH

As a kid, I wanted to be a doctor. I dreamt of helping others, of dedicating my life to the pursuit of health and wellness. The human body fascinated me, and I longed to learn everything I could about treating disease, illness, and injury. Little did I know that Allah was to accept my prayer, just not in the way I assumed it would be accepted – in the form of a conventional medical degree. Instead, I ended up enrolling in a Bachelor of Health Sciences to qualify as a Functional Medicine Practitioner.

I had made a friend who was studying acupuncture at the (then called) Australian College of Natural Medicine while I was completing my bachelor's degree. Back then, my goal was to transfer to medicine in my second year of study. We talked a lot about our courses: mine, its emphasis on science's relationship with the human body – a linear, mechanical approach to treat symptoms, to prevent deaths – and hers, its focus on the spiritual self and treating the cause (rather than the symptom) of disease. We were at diametrically conflictive ends of the health spectrum, but when she spoke of her studies, something resonated with me. I found the idea of treating illness holistically, rather than applying the linear model, very appealing. I was drawn to the process of uncovering and healing the root of a problem, rather than trying to mask it through traditional treatment avenues, like medication. (This is a calling for others – and an honourable one indeed. However, it did not resonate with me personally.)

So, when I got the offer to transfer to medicine, I did not pursue it. Some call it insanity. I say my calling was different, and that my intuition led me where I needed to be.

Thus began my journey into the wilderness of preventative and holistic medicine, at a time (over 16 years ago) when herbs were frowned upon, GPs knew best, and the only way to treat ailments was through modern medicine.

Of course, my parents did not understand. "At least be a pharmacist!" my dad had said. "You will have security, a 9 to 5, and a good salary!" But, I found within myself an innate power – an ability to acknowledge autonomy over what I really wanted to do, as opposed to what my family or society wanted –

that helped steer me in the direction that resonated with my heart and mind. I followed my gut and commenced a joint degree in Nutrition and Herbal Medicine at the Australian College of Natural Medicine.

From there, I began practising as a Functional Medicine Practitioner, eventually going on to complete my Master's in Food Sciences/Engineering. I started my own clinic, which is now purely online. Currently, I consult with children and women one-on-one in the areas of childhood illness, female reproductive illness, and pre-conceptive and post-conceptive care, focusing on nutrition, supplementation, and mindset coaching.

HOLISTIC V LINEAR TREATMENT

When it comes to holistic healing, the cause is always multifactorial. I have never come across a disease that is triggered by just one thing. Thus, there is no one drug that fits all, no magical pill that cures everything.

Holistic medicine focuses on discovering the root of the problem and healing it. Even if there are multiple causes, it is essential to delineate each of them so that treatment can be wholly effective. Without considering every slice of the pie, you have an incomplete and linear view of the disease. Therefore, your treatment is not one that can be comprehensive.

Of course, I acknowledge that the linear model was designed to prevent diagnosed diseases from worsening, and to treat serious symptoms that may otherwise debilitate someone. However, when symptoms are viewed in complete isolation, treatment is not as effective as it would be if they were considered holistically. For example, when you have a headache, do you ever stop to consider why? No! You just pop some pills and continue with your day. You might be experiencing dehydration, stress, muscle tension, or even an underlying medical condition. Perhaps you are struggling with food sensitivities triggered by immunoglobulin G (igG) intolerances or heavy metals. But, because you have masked the symptoms, you *never find out* the root of the problem. This means that even if you manage to subdue the symptoms, the affliction will perhaps never leave, or will return, sometimes with a vengeance.

I am not suggesting that taking pain relief for a headache is wrong – not at all. Quite frankly, I acknowledge that in certain circumstances it is the only way to function on a daily basis (until of course a holistic treatment plan is implemented and the cause(s) of the headache are eliminated from the body, or the body tissue is otherwise healed). The point is, we must consider the body *as a whole* if we want to experience our best physical, mental and spiritual capacity.

Short-term band aid solutions may keep us functioning, but they will not allow us to live to our full potential. Modern medicine needs to recalibrate the way it administers treatment and focus on healing the *cause* of the problem, rather than the symptoms that are exhibited.

I get that the struggle is real – it is very challenging to consider the vast array of causes for a presenting medical illness. However, if you ever want to truly heal, there is no other way out of the growing body of sicknesses we, as a community, are experiencing. Our medicines, technologies and treatments improve, yet illnesses that prevent our quality of life and that leave us dependent on drugs are on the rise.

THE RELATIONSHIP BETWEEN FOOD, THE MIND, AND THE BODY

It is no secret that the brain impacts the physical being. No one can come into physical health without first addressing their mental health.

This is because:

1. the mind has an innate influence over the body – science has proved this multiple times over (e.g. resonance).

2. a person who is not willing to make a psychological change, will not be ready for a physical one. It is unfortunately always easier and safer to stay a victim of your circumstances than to make an active change and empower yourself.

Often, when I begin to treat a health issue holistically, I will discover that the root of the problem is *not actually* related to any physical anomaly. It is – in fact – mental.

Let's take food and body related issues, for example.

Ninety-nine percent of the time, the women I work with have a very deep and emotional connection to food. Their whole lives they have been told to suppress their emotions – to put others before themselves, to compromise, to be the 'perfect' woman, wife, and mother. Because of this, they have grown up unable to express their true selves. They make themselves small and mould their identities to 'fit in' out of fear and convenience; out of assuming and growing up to believe that what others expect of them is more important than what they expect of themselves. So, to fill this emotional void, they turn to food.

Unlucky for them, food only temporarily fills this space – it briefly enhances the brain chemicals that make a person feel happy. Their brain cannot otherwise achieve this happiness. Not only is it disconnected with its authentic self, it is also completely unaware of the disconnection.

As a practitioner, I can give these clients the best diet, supplements, and lifestyle advice, but until their mindsets change, the physical body will stay the same. Even if someone follows the health advice to a tee, as soon as the problems come back – they have another fight with their husband, their child won't sleep, their baby has a fever, someone swore at them on social media, they didn't get enough likes on their Instagram selfie, they disagreed with somebody on a topic they hold close to their heart – guess what they're going to turn to for emotional support? Food!

For many of us, food is a lot more than just the sustenance we need to survive. It is comfort, support, happiness, distraction, and relief. Often, we turn to food to fill voids in other areas of our lives. This generally results in not only *eating* poor foods but *overeating* them.

Renowned Muslim doctor, theologian, and spiritual writer of the 11th century, Ibn Al-Qayyim, belonging to the orthodox Sunni jurisprudence, once said that illnesses are caused by:

1. consuming more food before the previous meal has been digested

2. consuming foods of little or no nutritional value

3. indulging in different foods that are complex in their composition.[1]

I am afraid to say we mostly all qualify for one (if not all) of the above-mentioned points.

To detach ourselves from emotional eating, we must first acknowledge and understand where that attachment comes from. Then, it is up to us to work through that response with self-compassion and self-love.

A classic example is this: a client comes to me and says, "I've been on a diet for years, but I continue to gain weight." For this client, the first thing they need to do is ask themselves these three questions:

What is the mental pattern that keeps creating the same physical identity that I am trying to detach myself from?

Why do I keep returning to unhealthy eating habits?

**What is it about consistent exercise and
healthy eating that I just can't cope with?**

The answers could be many things: a stressful home life, an unfulfilling career, dissatisfaction in a relationship, poor body image – the list goes on. It is up to the client to identify and then work through whatever part of her life that is causing the blockage.

This, again, brings us back to the concept of the blind men and the elephant. We must sit back objectively and take a bird's eye view of our state of health, because addressing one area, and not addressing the other, will never offer complete wellness and will always only provide a partial picture. You might be eating clean and exercising, but if you don't acknowledge your psyche – if you're not ready to confront your demons, or face your shadows – then you're never going to have an authentic connection with yourself or achieve optimum health.

With that in mind, what are some of the psychological factors that come into play when we are trying to achieve our health goals?

1. Lack of self love

Nine times out of ten, when we are staring down the barrel of our health goals, it is ultimately a lack of self-love that gets in our way of achieving them. This shortage of love not only makes it harder for us to stick to long-term targets that benefit us, but also leaves us reluctant to seek support and invest in our own health and happiness.

For example, a lot of people refuse to see a naturopath (or a coach, personal trainer, nutritionist, psychologist). Their response is that it is 'too expensive'. This is completely justified – life is expensive and if you're struggling to make ends meet, then these services are probably not at the top of your priority list.

However, if you still go out and spend $80 on a lipstick and $300 on a pair of shoes, then the reason is not that you 'can't afford' a naturopath, it's that you don't think your health and happiness is worth the investment. You don't have the money to invest in yourself in a *meaningful way*. This stems from a direct lack of self-worth – your priorities point you in other directions.

Let me give you a personal example. My mum and I had this conversation about a year ago, and she said something profound. I said to her, "Mum, you need to book your physio more consistently; you've got time, you've got money, you've got energy, you've got a car, you've got all the resources."

She said, "But it's too expensive."

Now, her physiotherapy only costs $50. But in her mind, she's so worthless that putting $50 toward her health is a waste of money. She would rather spend that on her grandchildren, or on doing shopping for the house, or on buying ingredients to make a nice dessert for the family.

Instead of handing over $50 to a physiotherapist every fortnight, my mum was spending the same amount buying toys for her grandchildren. Why? Because that's what drives her sense of self-worth and makes her feel empowered.

It's not that we don't have the money, it's that we don't think our money is worth being spent in a particular area.

This is common in a lot of us, especially when our self-worth is derived from external factors. We are willing to spend money sending our kids to extracurricular activities (because that's what influential mum bloggers do, and therefore if we do it too it will drive us to feel better about ourselves because that's where we get our sense of self-esteem from) but won't invest in our own learning; just like we are happy to shout our friends dinner, but refuse to fork out the extra cash for our own healthy meal plans. Whatever it is, we often think that the only way we will ever be satiated with happiness is if we keep doing things for others, because that's what drives our sense of self-worth. When we feel unworthy, spending money on our own wellbeing seems like a waste.

I had an epiphany once, and it was in relation to a confrontation I had with the client. It blew my socks off, and in hindsight I *thank God* that it happened. The conflict gave me the opportunity to make many changes within myself – to acknowledge my own traumas and lack of self-worth, and to then gain awareness around that lack of sense of worth and heal it. It also exposed my client's lack of self-worth, to me.

The client was unable to get pregnant, she was overweight and experienced chronic migraines. We performed a hair sample, which showed that she had very high levels of mercury in her system. This led me to the scientific assumption that mercury may be the cause of the problem.

We started a mercury detox, and her migraines became less frequent. Eventually, they disappeared entirely, and were replaced by slight headaches when she ate too much sugar or became dehydrated (i.e. the common reasons as to why you might have a headache). Alongside this, the client was suffering from multiple infections – one in her colon, one in her stomach, and one in her small intestine. I recommended that she eat less sugar to combat the infections, or else they would persist. She did not take up this recommendation. Instead, she justified her behaviour by saying that eating sugar helped her cope, that she only indulged a few times a week, and that eating sugar was *surely* not the reason as to why the infections were not resolving.

During a consultation one day, the client started crying and told me that I was the reason she was not pregnant because I had delayed her ability to get better. It was all my fault because I was not doing enough to change her health.

Now, the first thing I should have done was ground myself in my own knowledge and self-contentment: that the body will only go at the pace that it is able to go. No practitioner can speed that up. The only person who can speed up the process is *the client*, depending on how consistently they are following the strategies that are recommended (and even then, it will depend on how toxic the body is as to how fast or slow that process is). The practitioner might navigate. But if the practitioner asks the client to turn right and they turn left, they are not going to get the desired results.

But I didn't do that.

Instead, I cried.

My sense of self-worth came from how successful I was in my clinic, and 99% of the time I *was* very successful in my clinic. However, when I got the odd client that vomited negativity on me because they were not improving, I felt unable to cope – like I was a failure, a disappointment, not good enough.

In this woman's case, it was her refusal to see a psychologist that was ultimately inhibiting her progress. She had trauma around food, hence why she could not kick the sugar – sugar was her saviour, it was how she filled her emotional void. I had advised her that the only way forward was to see a therapist – the way she behaved around food would only change if she acknowledged *why* she had an emotional connection to it in the first place.

She would not do it – she refused to turn right. She would not accept that the responsibility was on her to stop consuming sugar, which could only happen after she dealt with her food trauma with the help of a qualified psychologist.

Every statement she made to me, I took completely to heart. My negative inner voice took over. *You're not good enough, you couldn't get this patient well,* my unrelenting standards barked at me. *It's been one and a half years and you're still not where you should be. Why hasn't this client gotten pregnant, Julide? She said you were too expensive, and she's right. You're not worth it.* I felt inadequate because my client hadn't achieved results.

The first thing I had to acknowledge with my therapist was that I wasn't responsible for *anyone's* level of health success – good, or bad. As much as it was not my fault if people did not achieve their desired results, it was also not necessarily to my credit if they did.

If I said turn right and the client did, then all credit goes to them. Supplements don't magically take themselves; lifestyle changes don't miraculously happen. It's the investment of time, money, consistency, and knowledge that really gets results. I accepted that I'm not the creator of all the good outcomes of patients. The real heroes are the ones who take on the advice and apply the changes.

On the flip side, if clients are not getting good results, then I'm also not to blame. It's not on me if they don't make the necessary changes. Outcomes don't just happen. You can't simply pop a pill for a couple of months and expect to get results.

Your sense of self-worth should only come from within. If it comes from an external factor, it's always going to be up and down, and you will never set yourself up for success in achieving your goals. In this client's case, she did not love herself enough to follow the steps that would have enabled her to achieve success. In mine, I had attached my worth to others and their opinions of me, which affected my behaviour as a practitioner.

2. Underlying food trauma

Our behaviour and mindset around food is often influenced by pain. Healing that pain will heal our relationship with food and health.

When we hear the word 'trauma', scenes of violence, sexual abuse and horrific accidents usually flood our minds. We think of car crashes, war, and death. Of course, these events are all traumatic. However, the trauma that I am going to touch on – the trauma most people experience – is not this type of trauma.

Trauma is the suffering that we deal with every day. It is the pain that has stemmed from our childhood and past experiences. Trauma is our response to years of unconscious parenting, unrelenting standards, and unsolicited opinions.

To have trauma doesn't necessarily mean that we spend every day crying, agonising over the past (though some of us may do this from time to time – or our entire lives for that matter). Experiencing the residual effects of trauma can be as simple as becoming triggered and reacting to something or someone in a specific way or demonstrating behaviour that is shaped by an event (or events) in our past.

Trauma is when you were crying as a toddler and were told to 'shut up' before you had processed your emotions. Trauma is hearing the media and society shame women for being 'too fat' or 'too skinny'. Trauma is being coerced into undertaking extracurricular activities that you have no interest in to feed your parents' egos. Trauma is learning that being 'you' isn't enough to receive love. Trauma is unwillingly moulding yourself into what you think you should be, rather than what and who you actually are.

Often, we are afraid to label our experiences as traumatic because we feel like they are not valid or painful enough to warrant it. We think that what happened to us 'wasn't that bad' and therefore we should reserve the space for those who 'had it worse'. Alas, this type of thinking breeds serious problems.

Do you remember when you were a child and your parents made you finish everything on your plate because you had to 'eat what you were given' and the 'kids in Africa were starving'? Maybe you make these sorts of comments to your own kids. Well, I hate to break it to you, but this is one *incredibly* common example of behaviour that can lead to food trauma.

Encouraging children to eat everything on their plate is not as harmless as it may seem. When children are encouraged to eat past fullness, they:

1. learn to disconnect from their ability to acknowledge satiety, and

2. develop emotional relationships with food.

Let me explain.

Children obey their parents out of fear, guilt, and desire to please. When parents reward or punish children for finishing (or not finishing) a meal, they are attaching these emotions to food. For example, if a child is forced to sit at the table until they have eaten everything on their plate, they will be fearful of not finishing food in the future, learning not to trust their physical feelings of satiation. Conversely, if a child receives praise for eating past fullness, they will associate overeating with positive outcomes (praise) and learn to attach happy feelings to eating to excess (this is one of the many drivers of our current obesity epidemic).

These emotions disconnect the child from their intuitive gut. As we grow older, this translates to an emotional and unhealthy relationship with food whereby it becomes a means of contentment. Whether we have a void that can be attributed to a lack of self-love, a lack of self-worth, or a lack of a sense of belonging, we turn to food because it *momentarily* comforts us and makes us feel better. We then experience feelings of guilt and shame because we have consumed foods in amounts that we intuitively know are not of benefit to us.

When we are repetitively forced to keep eating as children, we learn to ignore our bodies' signals that tell us we are full. This suppresses our natural appetite later in life. We don't know when to stop, which can lead to a plethora of physical problems (obesity, type 2 diabetes, and cardiovascular disease) and psychological problems (disordered eating, depression, and anxiety).

3. Poor body image

The media can have lasting negative impacts on both adult and child relationships with food and body image through constant displays of what is 'acceptable' and 'attractive'. You know those trashy magazines that litter the supermarket registers? The ones that say celebrity X is too fat and superstar Y is too skinny? Just like they make us feel worthless, they imprint unattainable body standards on our children. Again, this breeds poor physical and mental health – as we strive to achieve the unachievable, as we look in the mirror and know that we will never be enough.

Back in the late 1990s and early 2000s, the 'desirable' western female body type was ultra-thin and ultra-blonde. This saw women everywhere starving and bleaching themselves to attain the unattainable. Twenty years later, and we are seeing a new (and arguably less realistic) trend emerge – the 'perfect hourglass'. This body shape accentuates the chest and buttocks, while the waist remains as thin as possible. Though there are those naturally born with thin or hourglass figures, there are far more of us who sit outside of these specifications – whether we have smaller hips, bigger thighs, or a double chin. Every body shape is beautiful, but the media does not want us to think that, because if you are perfect, then there is no money to make off you. Body confidence would mean a huge plummet in makeup, cosmetic surgery and skincare sales, resulting in billions of dollars of lost revenue. People would start to appreciate their own unique creation. They would be happy with whatever was given to them by God – whatever eye colour, nose shape, and skin colour they were born with – and a generation of confident, content, and happy humans that could not be controlled would be born.

But, we don't want that, do we? Body diversity is not showcased, leading us to consider ourselves as less than, as unattractive, as unlovable.

Similarly, the way we discuss physicality with each other perpetuates impossible body standards. When we shame our own (or others') bodies and talk about food negatively to one another (and in front of children) we become gradually traumatised. This can lead to disordered eating behaviours, low self-esteem, anxiety, and depression.

My mother was one of those women who purchased every new weight-loss fad – the lemon detox diet, herbal laxatives, you name it, she tried it – and none of them ever worked. In my eyes, my mother was perfect (in fact, I don't remember her *ever* being overweight). I remember looking at her and her photos and thinking, *Wow she is so beautiful I can't wait to grow up and be as bold and beautiful as her.* But she perceived herself as fat, as unattractive – as all of these things that simply weren't true. Now, all that said to me as a kid was that weight was a bad thing and that being overweight was something shameful. (I don't blame my mum for this. She was dealing with some severe image and self-esteem issues – a result of her having six children in the space of ten years. Of course, her body had changed quite significantly. During that time, she had also migrated from Turkey to a country whose people, culture, and food was all foreign to her.)

As a result, when I was in my second year of university, I started the habit of vomiting every time I ate (I never binged; I only ate and regurgitated my usual meals). I wasn't overweight by any stretch of the imagination, but I was so fearful of 'getting fat' that I vomited as a preventative measure. I had a lot of shame attached to my body, stemming from my upbringing. In fact, I remember that no one ever acknowledged my 'heavier' female family members outside of their physical appearance. Though I hated making myself vomit, the habit continued for several months. (Eventually, I stopped because I grew tired of activating my gag reflex and using it as a method to manage my weight.)

Now, at face value, one would assume I was making myself vomit because I was physically trying to lose weight. But, by looking holistically at my condition, we can see that the root of the problem was not actually a physical issue, but a deep shame and fear that if I gained weight, I would be worthless and unattractive and I would not fit in – the lone sheep never survives.

It is important that we heal the cause of our health issues (in my case, food and body shame) so that we take the appropriate steps toward treating the outward condition (vomiting up food that I had consumed). It is not just for our own health that we must do this, but also so that we don't carry our unhealed trauma with us and project it onto our children. Imagine if I had not taken the steps to heal my negative body issues. What sort of example would that set for my own kids – if they had heard me complain about my body, or witnessed me vomiting?

Children can be extremely impressionable. So, when Mum says, "I'm ugly, I'm fat, I'm no good," your child (who thinks you are perfect in every way possible) is going to think, *If Mum thinks she's so ugly, what does that say about me? I must be ugly too.* Or they end up growing up too fast – investing their time and energy into trying to make you feel better about yourself, which is not and should never be your child's job. It is this ingrained ancestral trauma that continues the chain of low self-worth, which ultimately promotes unhealthy relationships with food and food-related health problems.

WHY IT'S IMPORTANT TO BREAK THE CYCLE
Physical health implications

For as long as food is our forte and emotional comfort, we will forever breed disease. When we constantly eat unhealthy foods, in amounts and at times that we shouldn't, we put a huge strain on the body and the plethora of problems, if they do not show up immediately, accumulate. The liver works harder, the stomach produces extra acid, and the body requires more sleep to rest and recuperate. Then the bowels go into overdrive trying to expel the excess toxic load. Suddenly, your physical energy is expended cleaning out toxins rather than recuperating and rejuvenating the body. Overeating might make us feel sluggish, drowsy, and uncomfortable. Some people may also experience gastrointestinal issues, like irregular bowel movements, bloating, gas, reflux. We may also experience brain-fog and poor concentration, which affects every avenue of our lives.

When we regularly consume poor-quality food, we start experiencing more severe symptoms than those listed above. For example, eating again prior to digestion means that we consume more calories than what our body needs. This can cause weight gain and obesity, which can in turn lead to cardiovascular disease, cancer, hypertension, and type 2 diabetes.[2] Overeating may also disturb our ability to absorb the nutrients in our food, make our liver and pancreas work harder, and produce more bile and enzymes.

Mental health implications

As we now know, the negative information we receive about food and body as children can develop into health issues later in life. Though we can't turn back the clock when it comes to our own lives, we can actively try and heal our relationship with food, so that our traumas are not passed onto the next generation.

It may surprise you then, that (as well as what we have discussed above) there are many other (seemingly inconsequential) ways that we can negatively shape a child's relationship with food.

1. Attaching 'good' and 'bad' labels to foods

This is a tricky one. Of course, you want your child to eat high quality foods, so you tell them which are good, and which are not. You might even lure your child to eat their carrots (a 'good food') with the inducement of ice cream (a 'treat'). I hate to break it to you, but this breeds problems for your child, as they begin to attach their worth to the foods they consume (i.e. 'I ate bad food, therefore I am bad').

Instead, it is important to neutralise the way you talk about food. Instead of referring to foods as 'good' and 'bad', try referring to traditionally healthy foods as 'nutritious' and 'delicious', and stereotypically 'bad foods' as 'pleasurable' and 'comforting'.

When we remove the stigma from certain foods, we detach feelings of shame, guilt, and loathing. This can help us lead healthier lives, both physically and mentally. When we call food a 'treat' then our children want to please us to achieve that treat. Thus, they may do something just to make us happy, and as a result develop people-pleasing personality traits.

How often have you 'succumbed to temptation' by eating 'bad food'? I'm guessing many times. There is, of course, nothing wrong with this. However, if we have attached negativity to that food, we will immediately feel ashamed after we have consumed it. For some, it can ruin their entire day.

The converse of this is that when we eat foods that we consider to be bad, we can ultimately end up consuming *more*. We think Oh well, *I've gone and done it now,* when we snack on a bowl of ice cream. *I may as well finish off the tub!*

2. *Restricting or prohibiting certain foods*

The more limits we place on food, the more desirable it becomes.

When I was a kid, my parents didn't let us have soft drinks – we were never allowed Coke, never allowed to go to McDonalds. No surprises, we grew up *resenting* those rules. And, of course, once we could go out into the world and buy our own Coke and our own cheeseburgers, we did.

Now, I'm not saying that parents should completely forgo the good nutrition of their children. After all, we each carry the responsibility to keep our kids well fed, healthy and exercised. *However,* it is undeniable that the more you restrict something, the more enticing it becomes. The minute you detach emotion from food, is the same minute that it comes off the pedestal. This is true of everyone, but especially of children.

It is very important to verbalise and have discussions around why certain foods are prohibited, or why a food should not be eaten by the bucketloads, in an age-appropriate manner. This is how we can set our children up to have the intellectual capacity and resilience when they are faced with options that may be harmful to their health.

In the case of my parents, this was undeniably accurate. Though they did not allow us to have takeaway foods and sugary drinks, they took the time to explain to us *why* we could not have those things, rather than applying a 'no argument' disciplinarian approach. After we had tasted those foods, we no longer had a desire to continue consuming them, as we understood the reason as to why they were denied in the first place. Had my parents just said "no" to certain foods without explanation, the end result would likely have been different.

To be completely honest, I don't want my kids to eat hot chips. But, once a week, if they ask me for hot chips, I'm going to get them hot chips. I'm not going to make them miss out and resent me and the food I cook. That would only add fuel to their desire for chips, and if they finally did get them, they would be more likely to binge. They might even experience feelings of shame after eating because 'Mum told me no' their whole life.

Rather than prohibiting specific foods, try explaining their contents and the effect that they have on the human body. Do this in a neutral way and let your child know that it is ultimately up to them to decide what goes into their body. How much detail you provide will be dependent upon the maturity and age of your child.

For example, when it comes to my kids, I explain to them (in basic terms – they are still quite young) what chemicals are, when they are found in foods, and how they can affect the human body. This means that when they are confronted with a food choice, they can make an informed and autonomous decision about whether they want to consume that food. Whatever decision they make receives a neutral reaction.

For example, my daughter and I were out somewhere once, and she wanted a lollipop. I suggested that we look at the ingredient list on the wrapper (which was actually quite hard to find and read). Then she said, "It has numbers and chemicals, Mum."

"Yes, Elisa, it does," I replied. "I don't think you should eat it. What do you think?"

"Mum, I know I shouldn't eat it, but I really feel like it. It looks so delicious."

"That's up to you," I said. "Why don't you take this lollipop and have some licks until you decide you are done?" She happily agreed.

She started to lick, continuing for the next couple of minutes, and then handed me the lollipop. "Here you go, Mum," she said. "I don't like sugar. I don't want to finish this lollipop anymore."

I knew she would only have a few licks of the lollipop and then leave it. But, I wanted her to know that it was *her choice* to do so. So, there was my four-year-old, discarding a lollipop that she knew was not the best choice for her health, while still taking a small taste to honour her desire.

3. Removing children's autonomy around food

As I mentioned above, giving your child the autonomy to decide what to put into their body (within boundaries, of course) will give them the tools to make healthier choices.

The other side of this, is that when a child is young, the only autonomy they have is in relation to food and sleep. They don't have control over much else in their lives – the adults decide everything. So, when we take away that control from them, they may react in other areas.

I noticed this in my own child. When I was more restrictive in my approach to food, my daughter started making some conscious behavioural changes. For example, she started overreacting to minor things and was showing a low level of patience that she wasn't before. When I eased my approach and gave her back some control, she felt more liberated, and the resistance melted away.

You need to give your child some level of autonomy so you can promote their resilience, rather than just oppressing them with your power and 'discipline'. This will equip them with the strength and ability to make conscious decisions as they grow. We need to teach our children to learn right from wrong by empowering them to make their own choices.

When we, as parents, are driven by our egos, it is harder to see our own mistakes through the darkness. The only way forward is being okay with the fact that you will make mistakes, so that when you reflect in hindsight you can see where the error was and address it accordingly, rather than ignore it or purely have no consciousness over it.

4. Attaching meaning where there isn't any

It's not what happens to you that matters. What's important is how you *translate* what happens to you.

Our past life experiences influence how we respond to future situations. Everyone will experience hurt, loss, fear, grief, and anger in their lives. These experiences and feelings mould us (for better or worse) into who we are today. We can either choose to heal and learn from these experiences, or we can let them drag us down by influencing our future thoughts and behaviours in a negative way.

Often, those who don't heal from life experiences will project their unresolved traumas onto others. This may come in the form of attaching meaning to words, behaviours, or situations where there isn't any, or misinterpreting the intended meaning.

Therefore, you can say the same thing, using the same words, in the same tone, to two different people and receive two different reactions. This is because each person is projecting their unhealed traumas onto you via the statement you are making. Their translation of what you have said is dependent upon the filters that they have switched on relative to their previous experiences.

For example, if you say "You really shouldn't eat that chocolate bar" to a child who has been constantly belittled about their weight, that child is going to be flooded with shameful thoughts: *They are telling me not to eat the candy because I am fat, and that means that I am ugly. This chocolate bar will make me even fatter, and uglier, and more worthless.* This is because their past experiences (being bullied about their weight) has activated certain filters in their mind (any comment in relation to food is an attack on them and their body, even if that was not the intention at all).

Now, when you say the same thing to a child who has not been bullied about their weight, but has been educated about healthy eating, they will not attach this meaning, or feel shame. They will most likely think that the request is fair, and will be able to discern the true reasoning behind it – "Mum said I shouldn't because I had some chocolate earlier in the day"; "It's almost dinner time, so Mum probably doesn't want me to ruin my appetite"; "It has a chemical in it that I am allergic to, so I can't eat it."

Resolving our own trauma will lead to better eating habits, which will ensure that this trauma is not passed down to our children. By healing ourselves, we will be able to better guide our children, rather than adding to their poor relationship with food.

OPEN YOUR MIND

Everything is interconnected – what we think, what we do, and how our bodies respond. We cannot experience optimum health if we are not thriving in our physical, mental, and spiritual realms. This is not out of the box, or controversial – it's just *how it is.*

Unfortunately, this way of thinking is often not considered mainstream. As a result, holistic health often gets dismissed, or left in the dark.

I urge you to consider alternative treatments. We may all have the same anatomy, but our bodily responses that create disease can vary immensely. We functional medical practitioners do not see every man and woman as suffering the same ailment, or as having the same driving factors. We investigate each case on an individual and unique level, working to understand the psychological and contextual underpinnings of every patient.

For too long we have allowed an institutionalised medical system to pull apart our organs and treat our bodies as machines – throwing out a piece when it doesn't work as opposed to treating the cause of illness. As a result, we have created a space where people have more cancers and autoimmune illnesses than ever before, and our children are suffering from more ailments today than any child did 60 years ago. We must collectively look inward to discover how we can better our wellbeing and actively seek answers to our own health questions.

With that is mind:

Is there something you have not considered when it comes to your health?

Are you missing parts of the elephant?

Has a linear approach solved all of your issues, or have other issues risen to the top of the iceberg?

"HEALTH IS
LIKE MONEY,
WE NEVER
HAVE A TRUE
IDEA OF ITS
VALUE UNTIL
WE LOSE IT."

- JOSH BILLINGS -

THE TRUTH ABOUT WELLBEING

FUR WALE

Y SHIFT

FUR WALE

Fur Wale is living proof of how investing in your mental and emotional wellbeing can lead to a life of success beyond your imagination.

Fur Wale transitioned from being a Doctor of Natural Medicine to become a public speaker about self-empowerment and surviving the predicted disability of an autoimmune disease. Fur has created new benchmarks in the field of public speaking, speaking events and the future of feminine leadership with SHE Talks®, which has been featured in Arianna Huffington's magazine, recognised as 'Business of the Decade', endorsed by #1 Hall of Fame Speaker Tim Gard and partnered by Vision Australia.

Fur created the SHE Talks® platform in 2015 as a platform for women. Her vision is to enable women to transform the conversations of our culture because what we say or do not say will affect the wellbeing of generations to come.

Fur crafts and delivers highly impactful talks, workshops, virtual programs, events, resources and coaching for both men and women, founded in growth and development skills, and primal wisdom. As a result of Fur's life-changing knowledge, individuals accomplish success in all areas of their life and possess an unshakable foundation for life, upon which all skills can be set.

She has had the privilege of training more than 3,700 women. Fur, as an in-demand behavioural coach, was invited to mentor a women's AFL club to elevate their game and the wellbeing of the players' mindsets. Fur has spoken at events with audiences as large as 2,000 people for Lights Out and Homelessness Week and at Vision Australia Headquarters for International Women's Day.

Empowerment coach, public speaker, author, entrepreneur, RMIT business accelerator mentor, and in the top 1% of public speaking coaches in Australia, Fur embodies what it is to live life to the fullest of your potential.

You can connect with Fur at www.shetalks.com.au, info@shetalks.com.au, www.linkedin.com/in/shetalks, and on Instagram @she_talks_public_speaking.

RESTORING WHOLENESS WITH A CONSCIOUS METHOD OF SELF-REGULATION

What do health and wellbeing mean to you?

What is your relationship with wellness? What exactly do you want that you don't have?

Suppose you could have a much higher level of wellness, regardless of your age and circumstances. Would you make adjustments to your daily routine to build your reserve for wellbeing?

Living wellness requires proper guidance to achieve self-managed wellbeing. Your wellness will depend on the levels that you already have, want and need. Most of us want more than we currently have and need guidance to know what to do to get there.

MY PROMISE TO YOU

I am going to take you on a unique journey into your very own physical and mental landscape, to discover your potential for wellness. I will provide you with a framework for self-managing your well-being that will last you a lifetime.

You will develop a resourceful rapport with your body and mind as a self-regulating healing tool. I will teach you how to effectively manage external factors that impact your wellness by knowing what homeostasis is and what inhibits it. You will also learn how to use the placebo effect to your advantage, so that your potential for homeostasis functions optimally.

This will be developed through a four-step practical method for healing, a selection of transformative questions for you to answer, and one extraordinary practice from my foundation program. This is the simple and powerful daily practice I use at the core of my method for sustaining wellbeing.

YOU ARE IN CHARGE OF YOUR WELLBEING

We can often overlook what is not going well and dangerously ignore our natural healing power. We can chase an artificial image of wellness, instead of actually living it. Imagine who you could be if you knew exactly what to do to possess it.

Wellbeing is the state of being healthy and happy. It is defined by the ability to make the most of your lifestyle, circumstances, mindset, hereditary traits, and genes. Your potential for wellness is regulated by your behaviour and attitude and results in epigenetic changes in your body. This affects hormone messengers and gene expression, turning genes 'on' and 'off' and increasing or decreasing the risk of illness or disease.

The quality of your mindset and the body-mind connection is as essential as the quality of your lifestyle (day-to-day behaviours, activities and diet) in affecting hormone messengers and gene expression. However, we spend surprisingly little time focusing on the potential of our body-mind connection for wellbeing.

I want to help you change this and put the power back into your hands.

THE BODY'S REMARKABLE PRECISION FOR WELLBEING

Homeostasis is the intelligent regulating system that maintains the body's internal environment within set limits. Homeostasis has only one job – to seek wellness.

Your homeostasis maintains physiological balance to keep your body in a constant state of health and happiness, maintaining balanced internal conditions that allow you to adapt and to survive in the face of a changing and sometimes hostile internal and external environment.

Homeostasis is impeded by one factor – stress. However, even when stressed, we always have the capacity to define our possibility for wellbeing. Everyone has more significant potential for healing and wellness than they do for illness or disease. We all have the capacity to be in far better shape than our genes predispose, and we can achieve this by utilising the natural intelligence of homeostasis to establish balance.

There is a conscious connection between what we do and think, and how the body responds to maintain this balance. I call it *conscious self-regulation*. The practice of self-regulation supports the body's potential for homeostasis so that wellbeing is sustained.

THE POTENTIAL FOR WELLBEING IS SELF-MANAGED

In my studies of Natural Medicine and Human Behaviour, effective therapy is directed toward re-establishing the body's regulation state of homeostasis. Balance is obtained through allostasis: this means subtracting what is in excess and adding what is deficient to promote balance. When the body is not overloaded with toxins or overeating and the biological needs have been met, combined with conscious self-regulation of attitude towards health, the body can achieve homeostasis.

In the pursuit of long-term goals such as wellness, self-regulation involves managing our reactions to feelings, thoughts, beliefs and disruptive emotions influencing our behaviour over matters of importance. This self-regulation solves these issues we face that can stand in the way of homeostasis doing its job.

THE BODY-MIND CONNECTION AND SELF-REGULATION

A large part of my interest in self-regulation came from childhood. My understanding of the relationship between self-regulation and wellness was initiated by my father. He instilled the traditional wisdom he learnt when he was raised on an island during his formative years. In this community, when children hurt themselves, the elders didn't baby them. Instead, elders guided children to assess and manage the situation calmly.

My parents were both wise and worldly in raising my two brothers and me. We were encouraged to regulate emotions and behaviour through open conversations, with respect for our individuality. This gave us our very own foundation for self-regulation, according to our individual needs.

Left with a desire to master the practice of self-regulation, I taught my siblings conscious self-regulation practices, with their permission. This included a method of play to test our ability for mind and body control. I would ask my brothers to relax as I guided them to visualise twisting from the waist. I would then request they open their eyes and perform the action. They were always surprised at the remarkable difference in their ability. This guided-imagery practice was just one of the many research activities I carried out from the age of ten until I was sixteen.

I applied self-regulation to every situation. It became an invaluable tool for me in sports and when my mother passed. Self-regulation became essential for my survival, and it soothed my brothers' grief. Each evening, I would sit and read Shakespeare to put their focus on something else until they peacefully fell asleep.

Through mentorship and adversity, I came to know the greatest tool for well-being that is within every individual. I was mentally equipped to face challenges, moderate my moods and set boundaries for my wellbeing.

WELLBEING DOES NOT HAVE TO BE COMPLICATED

Growing up, I identified as being a healthy child. That's because to me, wellbeing meant having enough energy to robustly express myself and explore life.

At this stage, no one had any idea that I was running around with a genetic disorder. However, in hindsight, there were clear indications of an underlying issue with inflammation. Other children called me 'beetroot face' because I would overheat after exertion.

Some time later, I was given a diagnosis and told that there was nothing medical that could be done to resolve my rare genetic disorder. Faced with that uncertainty, I was left with two choices: I could accept the medical prognosis and live out the dire prediction, or I could find another way. I chose to preside over my health, and it led me to make a discovery that radically altered my life.

BREACHING THE RULES – IMBALANCE

When I breached my own rules and ignored my self-regulation practice, my health spiralled out of control. I was working extremely long hours that were mentally and physically taxing. I was so busy that I disregarded my body's indications of stress.

One evening as I was closing the office door, something pulled in my groin as I stepped down from the patio. The weight on my hip caused intense pain. Lifting my leg felt even worse. The following day, I could barely get myself up out of bed.

This problem worsened, so I sought some medical tests. I was ready to explore the underlying reason for these extreme changes in my body. The doctor recommended an MRI to search for a brain tumour, as was medical protocol based on my family history. My mother had died from a brain tumour at 36 years old. I found myself surprisingly relieved when my results came back negative.

Continuing with the doctor's recommendations, I received blood tests. The results showed that I had the HLA-B27 gene marker, causing auto-immune disease and chronic inflammation. The doctor said, "Sorry to say, but you are one of the rare 0.8% of people who are positive for HLA-B27, and there's no cure. You have to know that your bones are going to dissolve and you will end up in a wheelchair." I was dismayed by the doctor's diagnosis.

I continued with scans on every organ of my body, to test for the effects of associated degenerative inflammation. I considered myself to be, in a sense, invincible and besides, I possessed the knowledge of how to manage my health. I wanted to solve this and I was determined to get back on track.

Each result came back clear – until my eye tests. They revealed inflammation that was damaging the middle tissues and causing blindness. More tests revealed an associated risk of rheumatoid arthritis and myeloid leukaemia. I heard myself say, "Is that why all of my bones will break down?" as though I was accepting the prognosis.

The following day, I found myself hunched over and unable to bend down to pull my pants on. I had to put them on the floor, sitting to gently manoeuvre my legs into them. Suddenly, nerves in my body began firing off. My face was flooded with a painful sensation like it was a pincushion; fine sharp stabs washed down my entire body. I felt as though I was going to pass out. It was terrifying.

Later that day, tests showed that my white and red blood count had dropped – significant inflammation was wreaking havoc in my body. I was stressed about having to live my life this way. It was exhausting and heart breaking. I was losing trust in my ability to survive it. This disease had crept slowly into my life until it was all that I knew. This was an unbelievable contradiction to who I was before the diagnosis.

I AM NOT MY ILLNESS

It was time to find my way back to myself, to stop denying that powerful force that seeks wellness. When we are disconnected from our most authentic self (the infinite intelligent potential within us) and instead focus on unhealthy or un-resourceful feelings and narratives, we separate ourselves from this potential.

I began drawing upon all of my formal education in the sciences of natural medicine and my knowledge of self-regulation, and I began listening to my body with compassion – consciously being warm and understanding towards the pain in my body and simply letting it be there. I was essentially reducing the stress and tension levels that were exacerbating the condition.

The smallest conscious shift towards wellness made the pain dial down moderately. And, without the negative story about what the pain meant or the added tension, I could shift pain considerably. When I caught my feelings and thoughts early, I would have mastery over the pain.

THE GREATER PART OF WELLBEING COMES FROM FEELING EMPOWERED

I started in life with a root belief that things are always working out for me, and I held myself to be invincible. Instead of living this, my thoughts had become, "What if I don't have any control over this disease?" When I got stuck in these thoughts and didn't feel invincible, I would doubt my potential for wellbeing. In this area of my life that was unfamiliar and scary, I became uncertain.

Fear of the past and fear of the unknown took me down a path of feelings and thinking that I ended up identifying with: a lack of wellbeing. So, I decided that fundamentally the only problem I had was a switched-on gene that I could begin to regulate – now I could be confident in my healing process.

Using my foundation practice, I took cues from my body as the need presented. This included requiring rest, certain foods, probiotics and eliminating stressors. I tapped into my potential for health and recovered quickly from my life-threatening issues.

The HLA-B27 gene that had flared up due to the persistent stress in my mind and body was now regulated. A CRP test showed no markers for inflammation and blood and saliva tests failed to identify the gene marker that I was born with. It had switched off.

Today, I live free from chronic pain and the 'giving up' mentality I got stuck in. I found 'peace of mind' and avoided that predicted downward spiral of ending up disabled. Because I trusted my potential for wellbeing more, I am living life instead of surviving it.

Some would say the changes in my health came from a spontaneous remission. I am here to tell you that I don't believe in spontaneous remission. I established my wellbeing by knowing my potential for wellness and following through with my practice.

There may be other challenges in the future that bring stress. In these cases, it will be necessary to face and manage well to prevent another flare up, and I am prepared.

I possess a healing method that defies my hereditary predisposition and chronological age. I moved beyond genetic and physical indicators for disease and achieved a better state of health and wellbeing. My life, health, relationships, businesses and future have been profoundly enriched by my practice.

THE DIARY OF MY PROGRESS

After one month, I experienced a 50% improvement in overall wellbeing.

After three months, the inflammation in my eyes halted. The risks of leukaemia and rheumatoid were no longer evident. The inflammation in my body significantly reduced. White and red blood counts improved from critically low levels, and my bone density improved. I felt like I could go out dancing again.

After one year, white and red blood counts had improved even more, and so had my bone density levels. I forgot what the intensity of the pain had felt like.

After two years, blood and saliva tests failed to identify the gene marker HLA-B27. My white and red blood cell counts were at normal levels, as was my bone density. My biological age was 13 years lower than my chronological age – I was healthier and fitter than my age or genes predisposed!

STRESS

Stress was the trigger for my disease. Medical research has identified chronic stress and inflammation as linked to every disease. When the stress response stays elevated longer than is necessary for survival, it takes a toll on all systems within the body.

Stress interferes with the production of chemical compounds in the body needed for our diet, supplementation and exercise to be highly effective. As a result, self-talk can make or break our health and fitness practices. Stressful emotions negatively impact our potential for health, which is why conscious self-regulation of the body and mind is the essential groundwork in any health plan.

THE NECESSITY OF BALANCE

The nervous system is where we have the most significant control. Our conscious mind is influential in regulating the nervous system and decreasing stress hormones. The sympathetic nervous system, which lies along the spinal cord, ramps up during stress and inflammation to prepare us for action during times of challenge and danger.

The main contributor to the parasympathetic nervous system is the vagus nerve. The most crucial role of this nerve is to regulate the functions of our brain, throat, heart, lungs, entire digestive system and influence how emotions such as fear and anxiety are processed to bring calm to the body and mind.

The vagus nerve can become irritated over time and lose its 'tone'. As we get stressed, tiny sacs of air in the lungs collapse. If you find yourself double inhaling, sighing heavily or yawning without feeling tired, you have an overstimulated vagus nerve.

Higher vagal tone improves health and longevity of life, including through increased emotional stability, better blood sugar regulation, reduced risk of cardiovascular disease, improved gut health and a reduction of migraines and unrelated pain.

You can improve vagal tone with these vagus nerve-calming practices:

- Soothingly holding your neck

- Humming to stimulate the vocal cords

- Massaging the face, neck and behind the ears

- Taking a deep breath in and exhaling with an audible sigh

- Placing an ice pack around your neck or on your forehead

- Moving calmly, using tai chi, yoga, or mantra meditation

- Experiencing a full belly laugh and using positive self-soothing practices

- Exhaling from the mouth against a partly closed airway (throat)

- Practising the Valsalva manoeuvre by pinching the nose while trying to breathe

- Practising panoramic vision (optic flow) by looking deep into the horizon, gazing left to right

- Plunging into cold water, taking a cold shower or splashing cold water on your face and neck

THE GUT-BRAIN CONNECTION

Activating healthy gut microbiome is critical in having high vagal tone. This can be achieved through the use of fermented, pre-digested and activated foods and probiotics.

The gut-brain connection manages immunity and inflammation. An overgrowth of unhealthy bacteria causes toxins to pass from the gut into the blood and causes inflammation. This imbalance reduces the ability to absorb nutrients, decreases intestinal activity that delays bowel motility, leading to constipation. Notably, your gut's inability to create Gamma-Aminobutyric Acid (GABA), can leave you emotionally out of control with your mind racing.

THE BODY-BRAIN CONNECTION

The body and brain are a feedback loop. The peripheral nervous system, which lies outside the brain and spinal cord, receives information from our senses and responds to physical sensations in our body.

Humans are meaning-making creatures who interpret these physical sensations based on our thoughts and beliefs about what those sensations could mean. We predict whether those sensations mean 'everything is okay' or if they are an alert that something is wrong. Stress hormones continue circulating when you get stuck in emotions such as 'something is wrong' or 'hopelessness', which keeps you mentally ruminating and physically tired.

You can moderate stress hormones with your body and your mind. Engaging in something physically exerting and mentally regaining control by being purposeful and creating a strategy for a better outcome bolsters your confidence to move forward.

GRIEF IMPEDES HOMEOSTASIS

Life will continue to present obstacles, and sometimes we are overcome by them and feel at a loss. In the absence of joyfulness, we can experience forms of grief, such as disappointment. This emotional response is a significant factor in stress-driven inflammation.

Collective grief has emerged since the COVID way of life. The loss of 'life as we know it' means that we are now experiencing a loss of normalcy and anticipatory grief – that feeling you get when you are uncertain what the future holds. COVID has caused a rise in stress-driven inflammation. This new way of life needs to be adapted to, to ensure our wellbeing.

Receiving a prognosis can feel like a loss of normality, with our right to choose taken away; it can be very distressing. I will never forget going through the five stages of grief when I received my prognosis. The first stage is shock and denial, and I was in denial for a long time. Meanwhile, the symptoms were progressively getting worse. It is vital to consciously adapt and move through grief from the loss of wellbeing.

CEREBRAL BODY-MIND BASED EXPERIENCE

When we function from a lack of wellbeing, it can make us irritable and we can perceive everything as difficult. Muscles contract and pinch off nerves, impeding their ability to freely communicate with the brain and the rest of the body to produce balance.

When we are free from this unhealthy and lacking mindset, the brain chemistry increases immune competence and health-promoting blood flow. We feel expanded, stand taller in more open stances, breathe more fully, smile and laugh more, think beyond negative bias, and feel empowered and enthusiastic because we have more energy. We have tapped into our potential.

Adopting these physical traits, such as an upright and open posture, are strong predictors for improving self-regulation of our mind to support homeostasis to function optimally.

THE EXPECTANCY EFFECT: USING THE MIND AS A HEALING TOOL

The mind has a powerful influence over the body when we believe in the treatment, and can get our body to produce actual therapeutic results. This is a phenomenon called the placebo effect.

The placebo effect works on symptoms regulated by the brain and is undeniably the most potent self-regulating tool.

The placebo effect is not positive thinking or repeatedly saying that you will get better when you don't believe you will. Repeating a positive statement that you don't fully believe triggers and heightens what I call 'the critical mind'. The part of our brain that aims for survival has a bias towards negativity, and it provides us with all of the reasons we can't get better. The placebo is a belief that we believe in with positive expectancy.

Suppose you say, "Cake makes me fat." In that case, the stress of believing something terrible is happening to you and the accompanying guilt increases cortisol, the stress hormone which increases fat.

THE MOST POWERFUL FORCE IS OUR BELIEFS

A remarkable example of the placebo effect on the body-mind connection is a study by psychologist Daniel Goleman on people with multiple personalities.

Goleman found that each personality within the one individual presented significantly different physiological responses, traits and diseases.

Another example is the famous mentalist Derren Brown, who demonstrated how hypnotising someone not to notice the cold while plunging their body into an ice bath for several minutes is a potent analgesic and removes the mental message of pain.

Elite sports coaches worldwide have discovered that optimal performance is mentally contingent upon 'psyching up' through encouraging and believing in yourself. The internal commentary and imagery create anticipation of the desired outcome. The results are just as real as the external physical preparation and technical skill.

Consider, if you do not think you can run a four-minute-mile and believe your internal organs will burst if you do, you won't let yourself make it. Olympic athletes have failed to win because of the limits of conventional thinking. Roger Bannister taught us that we could shift a psychological barrier to shift a physical one and do what has never been done before. The defining difference for Roger was that with minimal physical training, he visualised himself running and seeing a clock-hand as he crossed the finish line in under four minutes. It's no surprise that Roger went on to become a neurologist.

HOMEOSTASIS MUST BE SUPPORTED

In my practice as a health advisor, I have discovered that the most effective treatment is always when the individual believes in their body's intelligence for wellbeing. They empower themselves by accepting something they had no say over, with the statement: 'Can't change it, I choose it', combined with the right strategy for healing.

This is my four-step strategy for healing:

1. RESTORE: Adopt a mindset of positive expectancy for wellbeing.

2. REMOVE: Excess nutrients, toxins, pathogens, drugs, negative emotions and invalidating thoughts.

3. ADD: Whatever is missing that would make the difference to your wellbeing (for example, improved quality lifestyle and healthy mindset).

4. ALLOW: Give your body time to come into alignment with your new
healthy mindset.

DISCOVER THE CURRENT STATE OF YOUR WELLBEING

Take a moment to acknowledge how you physically feel right now. Think about
what emotions and beliefs are running through your mind.

Over time, this practice assists you to feel more in touch with the needs of
your body. You will build a rich understanding of your body-mind connection
and how to consciously self-manage your wellbeing.

Ask yourself:

• What are the ways I am managing myself that impacts my wellbeing
physically and mentally?

• What are the unhealthy and healthy narratives I am telling myself?
(Make a list. Next to each one, write down how you are going to manage best
or promote those narratives.)

• Who am I mostly living life as? What are my commanding emotional
states? (Examples: disappointed/joyful, stuck/opportunistic.)

• Who don't I get to be? (Example: fun-loving me.)

THE PRECURSOR TO HEALTH

Conscious self-regulation is an increasingly important topic in the role
of wellness. Stress is not going away. We live in a world where we are
overstimulated, have more to do and where poor choices to self-soothe are
readily available.

While you may initially feel like life has dealt you a bad hand (like I felt
with my prognosis), it is not the hand you are dealt that is the biggest problem.
What matters more is your ability to cheer yourself up after a disappointment,
bounce back after bad news, remain calm under pressure, and act consistently
with the values that will support you.

Conscious self-regulation empowers any problem. In place of denial,
avoidance, resistance, anger, sadness, depression, or detachment, you process

the information you receive and determine how you are left feeling, whether that is empowered or disempowered.

DEVELOPING CONSCIOUS SELF-REGULATION FOUNDED ON SELF-COMPASSION

Conscious self-regulation is about establishing how you want to feel; it is never about self-judgement. If you value peace and joy, regulate what you give significance to, forgo complaining about your lot and avoid what is known as self-inflicted stress.

Self-regulation is a skill that you can learn through using goal-directed behaviours. It is a matter of consciously choosing to meet the goal, such as peace of mind and wellbeing, even in the face of challenges and without additional stress.

Conscious self-regulation is like a thermostat that keeps the room at a specific temperature. It tracks fluctuations, comparing them to the 'set-point' (goal), and knowing whether to move the value. Unlike the body's automated regulation of homeostasis, conscious self-regulation is a skill that we develop through continued practice.

SELF-FULFILLING PREDICTIONS: BELIEFS ARE BLUEPRINTS

We can get caught up in an opinion about ourselves and the world around us. We each have some form of 'not good enough' thoughts, because unconsciously, we function from a mindset of survival. That part of our brain feeds us all of what we can't do and what is not possible, to keep us safe in our comfort zone. We experience an internal conflict between what we hope is possible and what our mind tells us is not.

Consider, if you identify as less-than, stressed, stuck, depressed or anxious, that this feeling is self-fulfilling. If you are focused on what's not good or not working in your life, you will believe the future will be more of the same or worse. When you feel this way, it is crucial to consciously practice emotions, beliefs, and behaviours that align with your potential for wellbeing. I know that it is not always easy to make considered choices in the face of devastating emotions or circumstances, but for the sake of your wellbeing, you cannot let yourself stay too long in those stressful states.

When you understand the degree to which your emotions and beliefs affect your body, you begin to understand how fundamental it is to consciously focus them in a way that supports your potential for wellbeing. For example, neuroscientist Dr Caroline Leaf's life-long research established that as we interpret the world with our emotions, we are reinforcing healthy or unhealthy physical structures in the brain, which predict disease or wellbeing.

Your emotional state, beliefs, and the stories you tell yourself are the ceilings you live under.

Either your body-mind is free to function from the highest possibility, or your emotions, beliefs, and stories diminish, contradict, distort, and disconnect you from your potential for wellbeing.

Acknowledge 'negative' feelings as messages that something is needed. See a lack of wellbeing as a message from the body and mind that something is missing so that you can do something proactive that allows homeostatic balance to happen.

It is essential to actively and consciously self-regulate daily. This acts as a therapeutic tool to aid healing and wellness; *this* is how you define and sustain your wellbeing.

FEELING BETTER BY *KNOWING* BETTER

Your new life is going to cost you your attachment to the identity of lacking wellbeing. Be okay with that. Align with your infinitely intelligent core that knows you are whole, worthy, and abundant – live this as your very own *truest truth!* You will be training your body and mind for what the future feels like and establishing homeostatic resilience.

SHE TALKS® DAILY PRACTICE

The very moment that you wake, you get to make the most important decision of your day and perhaps your life, to sustain wellbeing. The following practice is a highly effective way to discover what is missing and achieve your goals.

Ask yourself: *What's missing that would make a difference to my wellbeing?*

This daily practice brings about a state of balance. You bypass survival thinking to access the higher intelligence centres of your brain without constraint from negative bias, so you can come up with unexpected solutions. I call this your *wise mind*.

One time when doing this practice, I had the vision of ingesting lots of probiotic powder. This was a brilliant insight from my body's intelligence, because a test revealed my gut biome had become critically unbalanced. Another time I received the thought, 'no beetroot'. As I came out of the practice, my first thought was that it was ridiculous. It turns out it wasn't. I have experienced many more similar instances that have proven correct.

To carry out this daily practice:

1. Ask in a lucid state
   Upon waking, keep your eyes closed and consciously remain relaxed or induce a lucid state by deep breaths with long exhales until you are relaxed.

2. Keep asking yourself
   Ask yourself the question, 'what's missing that would make a difference to my wellbeing?', with an intention of discovering the answer. I call this a state of calm discovery.
   - The answer/solution will come as a realisation. You may feel like it just makes sense, or you may feel it as a moment of truth.
   - The answer may arrive as a visual image, your internal voice, or a knowing. Its form may vary at different times.
   - If it is a command, demand, criticism or invalidation, you are in the critical mind instead of the higher intelligent centres.
   - Be patient with yourself during the practice. Remain in a state of positive expectation until you receive the answer.

3. Reinforce the practice
   An emotional state of calm joy and appreciation anchors the practice by releasing the endocrine system's 'reward' hormone. For this practice to be effective, carry out the solution. Only then is the power to restore wellbeing in your hands.

   After 63 days, you will find solutions that automatically appear as you are waking from sleep.

YOU ARE BALANCE WAITING TO HAPPEN

Life is not over once we get test results or bad news. It is not inevitable to fail at life because of a breakdown. We do not have to fall apart and curse our bodies when we get older. You are not the prognosis waiting to happen, you are balance waiting to happen.

You can live a life well-lived. It requires the willingness to go beyond fixed ideas, assumptions, conditioned responses, others' thoughts, and quick-fix solutions to make adjustments to your daily routine that build your reserve for wellbeing. We can bring this balance to any area of our lives.

SHE TALKS® CASE STUDY 2019 TO 2021

The SHE Talks platform has transformed 3,724 lives. One such life that benefited from the SHE Talks daily program is that of Anna.

On 5 August 2019, Anna woke with one consuming thought: "What's wrong with me?" Anna presented to me as passive; she had lost confidence in her ability to articulate her opinion. She carried shame and a fear of speaking up from childhood, causing her to pretend to have it all together while being reserved. This had deprived Anna of her wellbeing. Anna thought she should be further along in her success by now and was not living anywhere near her potential.

I assured Anna that through the SHE Talks program she would possess the essentials to effectively self-regulate her approach, develop confidence and know herself as an effective leader. I took Anna through my foundation program, teaching her daily practice and strategies to assist her in getting to that personal, empowered and authentic place of success.

The transformation occurred in the first session. I explored core elements of truth with Anna. I asked her to become sophisticated at accounting for her perceptions and where she was holding herself against the perceptions of others. After working through this, Anna's story no longer controlled her.

We continued with three more sessions to train Anna in strategies and a contingency plan. Eliminating Anna's fear gave her the capacity to pinpoint her higher values, so she could authentically, confidently and elegantly express her point of view.

Post-training, Anna overcame her inability to perform well at 'torturous' meetings, as she restored her competency in her communication and leadership. Anna became an exceptional manager who inspired, motivated and trained her team to execute activities and was acknowledged by top management for her strong performance. Now Anna has the courage to take on speaking roles. Anna said, "The main distinction I took away was authenticity. This concept was an unfamiliar one for me to put into practice. This training has transformed every area of my life."

Two years later, Anna possesses the skill of conscious self-regulation and is capable of creating her dream life. She is now an interviewer for a Melbourne podcast and confidently starting her own business. Anna remains connected to her potential for wellbeing and lets her wiser personality emerge. She said, "I am free from that fear that caused me to contract and doubt my potential since childhood. I no longer have that negative self-talk. That stress from two years ago that had me feeling small has left me. I know myself as confident and expanded." Since working together, Anna and I have remained close friends.

It is no mystery why I transitioned from being a naturopath to creating the programs I teach today. It thrills me to no end to share what I have discovered with Anna and all of my participants so they can be free to live their best and wisest life!

I INVITE YOU TO JOIN THE 63 DAY MORNING & EVENING MINDSET PROGRAM

The 63 day Morning & Evening Mindset program is a morning and evening practice that champions you to thrive all day and go to bed satisfied with your life. It is transformational and solves many problems that we face, grounding you each day in deep remembrance of who you are.

You are guided through recordings with a set of distinctions that give access to powerful resources hidden in the deepest parts of your mind to establish competence. By the end of the program, you will possess an unshakable foundation for life, upon which all skills can be set. It's a clear two-step process to finally eradicate the inner critic that's been holding you back.

SHE Talks participants have reported feeling tapped into their most potent tool for success. They become skilled in managing stress, never need to make excuses, live without worry, overwhelm or procrastination in their way, and are empowered daily. You can experience an immediate improvement with the most outstanding results after 63 days, because it takes 63 days for gene expression to alter!

The SHE Talks program gives you the complete framework for managing your wellbeing. Break through to who you were born to be and live a stress-free life.

This completes my promise.

"Do something today that your future self will thank you for."
Sean Patrick Flanery

"I HAVE CHOSEN TO BE HAPPY BECAUSE IT IS GOOD FOR MY HEALTH."

– VOLTAIRE –

YOUR
EXCEPTIONAL
LIFE

MARCUS PEARCE

Y SHIFT

MARCUS PEARCE

Marcus Pearce is magnificently obsessed with helping people create their exceptional life. A former smoking, binge-drinking journalist, radio and television producer, Marcus's media career included time at Leader newspapers, Sport 927 and SEN 1116 before concluding at Channel Nine and The AFL Footy Show in 2006.

Amongst writing hundreds of match reports, producing more than 1,000 radio shows and dozens of AFL Footy Shows, Marcus also covered major events including the 2004 Athens Olympics, 2006 Melbourne Commonwealth Games, the 2006 FIFA World Cup and multiple AFL Grand Finals.

His switch from sports media to health, wellness and personal growth media was seven years in the making.

In 2005 Marcus met his now-wife Sarah, a chiropractor, who was the catalyst of Marcus's health transformation from a Red Bull-guzzling, meat-eating smoker to a ginger-tea sipping teetotalling vegan, to somewhere back in the middle.

Marcus and Sarah spent most of 2006–07 overseas, living in a thatched cottage on 100 acres in Donegal, Ireland whilst running a chiropractic centre together. In 2008, on their return to Australia, they opened Pure Wisdom Chiropractic and Lifestyle.

In 2013 Marcus and Damian Kristof began the podcast *100 Not Out: Mastering The Art of Ageing Well*. In that same year, Marcus joined The Wellness Couch podcast network as the Executive Producer of events including The Wellness Summit. Since its inception, *100 Not Out* has recorded more than 400 episodes and has received almost one million downloads, whilst The Wellness Couch network surpassed 11 million listens in 2020.

In 2014 the time had arrived for Marcus to create Your Exceptional Life Blueprint framework. He created an online program and began sharing his insights and trainings both digitally and in-person.

Since then, Marcus's online courses have been consumed by over 20,000 people in 155 countries and he has delivered keynote presentations and trainings to companies as big as NAB all the way down to local communities.

In 2016, Marcus and his podcast co-host Damian travelled to the Greek island of Ikaria – also known as 'the island where people forget to die' – to host the inaugural *100 Not Out Longevity Experience*.

You can connect with Marcus at www.marcuspearce.com.au.

FROM RED BULL AND CIGARETTES TO GINGER TEA

Like many Australian children in the 1980s, I grew up on a daily diet of Rice Bubbles and two pieces of Vegemite toast for breakfast, two Mint Slices for morning tea, a stale white bread margarine-lathered peanut butter sandwich for lunch, Barbecue Shapes for afternoon tea, pasta for dinner, and ice cream with Milo for dessert. I have no memories of drinking water as a child; instead, I was constantly sipping on super sweet lemon cordial and soft drinks.

Ask 100 people born in the 1980s in Australia and I'm sure you'll find my childhood diet, whilst definitely unhealthy, was not uncommon for an Australian child growing up at that time.

My parents split up when I was 10, which was naturally heartbreaking. In hindsight it was the best decision they ever made. Ever since I can remember I knew I wanted to be a sports journalist. I studied journalism at university, worked in radio for five years before landing a plum job as Associate Producer of *The AFL Footy Show*, at the time the number one live television show in Australia. Whilst many closest to me may have felt this was the next big step of a lifetime media career, I was about to transform in a completely different way.

I had fallen in love with an incredible woman who was different to me in almost every way you can imagine. Sarah (now my beautiful wife) was a health professional with a high value on eating well, work-life balance, and an overall healthy lifestyle. I on the other hand was a work-hard, play-hard journalist who loved smoking, binge drinking and had an 'anything goes' laissez-faire relationship with food.

And whilst the sparks of romance were flying in all directions, my decade-long smoking habit and 'everything in generous moderation' health philosophy was not exactly advancing our relationship. One particularly distasteful experience took place early each Friday morning. *The Footy Show* went to air every Thursday night, and I'd return home in the early hours of the morning smelling like cigarettes and beer. Too tired to shower, I'd crawl straight into bed next to Sarah. My girlfriend of a few months would be startled awake by the disgusting stench that had entered her peaceful slumber. It was not a good look! After a number of agitated Friday morning conversations, I decided to do something about it.

My love of statistics would help me quit smoking. My three-cigarette per day habit had to sound and feel a whole lot worse than that. I calculated that three cigarettes per day was in fact over 1000 per year, and more than 10,000 per decade. If I was going to enjoy a lifetime relationship with Sarah and have children with her (and be a great example to them), then smoking just simply wasn't going to work. Without intending to oversimplify it, this understanding was all I needed to quit. I had to make smoking inconsistent with my identity.

My personal changes didn't stop with smoking. I also went on a 30-day meat-free challenge, and as a result my nickname at work went from 'MP' or 'Pearcey' to 'Mung Bean'! I swapped my morning tea Red Bull and cigarette for a freshly-grated ginger tea and cashew nuts, and the chicken schnitzel burger I once chowed down for lunch was now a chickpea curry and rice at the local Indian vegetarian café. By 2005 I was a non-smoking, five kilograms lighter vegetarian-soon-to-become vegan. I felt unstoppable. And at 24 years of age, I felt I'd reached enlightenment sooner than I expected. The secrets to longevity and an exceptional life were as simple as removing animal products and cigarettes (or at least that's what I thought).

In 2006 I said goodbye to the media, travelled the world with Sarah for 18 months, returned home to live by the sea in country Victoria, founded a wellness centre, got married, and started a family.

SEARCHING FOR THE FOUNTAIN OF YOUTH

By 2010 I was a raging vegan and truly believed that a vegan lifestyle (no meat, dairy, animal products of any kind – not even honey) was the official fountain of youth and key ingredient to a great long life. On top of that, I'd given up alcohol four years earlier and believed all alcohol was bad for you.

And then one night my world turned upside down. As a voracious reader and someone continually looking to have my views reaffirmed, I began reading a book called *Healthy at 100* by renowned vegan John Robbins (b. 1947). I expected this book to reaffirm to me that being a vegan was not only the best decision one could make in life, but also for longevity.

My beliefs were about to be slapped in the face.

Robbins grew up the heir to the throne of Baskin Robbins ice cream – a multi-billion-dollar global ice cream franchise you have most likely enjoyed at least once in your life. Robbins grew up eating ice cream for breakfast, lunch and dinner, spending his summer holidays playing in his ice cream shaped swimming pool, and being groomed to take over the family business.

Robbins didn't like what he was seeing though. His uncle, and co-founder, Burt Baskin, died of a heart attack at 54, and his father, Irv Robbins had diabetes, high blood pressure and high cholesterol. After renouncing himself from the family business, John and his wife, Deo, left for Canada, where they lived in a small hut, sprinkled cabbage seeds in the backyard, taught meditation and yoga for gold coin donations, and lived on their crops. In short, Robbins's life took a 180-degree turn, culminating in a career as an author of many books including *Healthy at 100*, *Diet For A New America* and *Food Revolution*.

I was no further into the book than page two of the introduction when my own life took a sharp turn. Robbins was referring to a study completed by the Yale School of Public Health. The results of it changed my life completely.

In the study, more than 600 men and women were asked multiple times over the course of 20 years whether they agreed with statements including: 'As you age you become less useful', 'As you age you become more of a liability', and 'As you age your best years are behind you'.[1]

What the study found was that the people who agreed with these statements had a disempowered view of ageing, dying on average 7.5 years earlier than those who disagreed. What fascinated me and sent shivers down my spine was that they didn't measure their exercise, genes, economic status, family life, careers or environmental factors.[2]

All they measured was a *belief*.

Most glaring of all for me, was that they didn't measure their diets. This hit me between the eyes. All it took was two pages from a book written by a legend of the vegan world to show me the fountain of youth did not live in our diet. The best thing about being a journalist is that I didn't take this personally. Instead of judging myself, I became intensely curious. The next day, I went to work at our wellness centre and paid particular attention to everyone coming in. I was on a mission to see if this belief of a disempowered future was as widespread as Robbins proclaimed.

One after another, all I heard from Sarah's patients was "I'm too old to do this" and "I'm too old to do that". I was shocked by how disempowered people had become all because of a number – and some of these people were only in their twenties and thirties.

I was so rocked by my findings that I decided to put my journalist hat back on and go on the hunt for people who were ageing well. I didn't want my research to start and end at our wellness centre or with the remote cultures Robbins had featured in his book. I wanted to find more relatable people living relatable lives.

"How you age is negotiable."
Dr Walter Bortz

A BLUEPRINT FOR LIFE REVEALS ITSELF

Research is a wonderful thing when you're learning information that inspires you. Minute by minute, day by day, I felt my beliefs changing about what it took to live an exceptional life. I was coming across human beings that were living simply remarkable lives, and whilst they were impacting me greatly, I just knew I had to share their stories with the world.

By 2012, podcasts had become a great way to share a message, and so without more than a moment's thought, I called my good friend Dr Damian Kristof, a health professional and media identity in Melbourne who was 39-about-to-turn-40 and not looking forward to it. I pitched the idea of co-hosting a podcast on longevity. He said yes, and we were off. The *100 Not Out* podcast was born.

As a vegan (and despite my epiphany), I still believed that we would find a vegan diet to be a strong precursor to both quantity and quality of life. Damian, a strict omnivore (meat, grains, vegetables, dairy, nuts and seeds), held the view that we would find that this style of eating was the most important factor in living a long life.

We conducted our first 12 interviews in less than two days, and it was clear that our respective biases were anecdotally being smashed to pieces. Ruth Frith, who won World Masters Athletics gold medals at 101, didn't eat vegetables. Fitness fanatic and Australian football legend, Tommy Hafey, ate ice cream every day. Octogenarian Mimi Kirk meanwhile had moved from a vegetarian diet to vegan diet in order to improve her arthritis, and thrived.

With every passing guest a blueprint for living a great, long life was revealing itself. Diet was *not* the number one ingredient. In fact, founders and formulators of the internationally acclaimed Atkins, South Beach and Pritikin diet all died at 72 or younger. And if our guests were anything to go by, movement in any form was far more important than society, medicine and governments had been telling us.

But it wasn't as simple as working out the importance of diet versus exercise. What about career choice, relationships, wealth and spirituality? Where did they fit into the hierarchy of living a great life? What impact did stress and trauma have on longevity? I asked myself these questions for years, interviewing dozens of living legends in search of the answers. Countless nights were spent pondering the research, and eventually it struck me that no matter your genes, upbringing, race, religion, culture, financial status or diet, there was a pattern – a blueprint – for being truly exceptional in each area of life and not just one. It was at that moment the Exceptional Life Blueprint was born.

Before we dive deep into this blueprint, allow me to introduce you to the people who inspired it – people I like to call *The Exceptionals*.

The Exceptionals are the small percentage of humanity who make the rest of their life the best of their life, no matter what has happened in the past. In this chapter, I hope to illuminate what it takes to be an *Exceptional*: we all can incorporate movement into our lives, make health and movement a priority, not overcommit, and eat in accordance with our values.

To be an *Exceptional* you don't need extreme wealth, fame, beauty or the best genes. Instead, membership to this exclusive club requires that you question the many conventional and limiting beliefs thrust upon you by a unique yet overwhelming selection of family, friends, colleagues, media and society as a whole.

THE EXCEPTIONAL LIFE BLUEPRINT

If you think about life as a recipe and you are the chef, then imagine your Exceptional Life Blueprint as a dish with eight ingredients –

1. Life Purpose/career

2. Movement

3. Social Life

4. Nutrition

5. Family

6. Growth

7. Wealth

8. Spirit

The order of which you put each ingredient into your life and the amount of each has a major impact. Do you prioritise wealth over family and friends? What happens if you put in too much work and not enough family or nutrition? How does the recipe of life taste if you put family first and your spirit last? I have battled, experimented with and explored these conundrums for years. And finally, here is what I discovered.

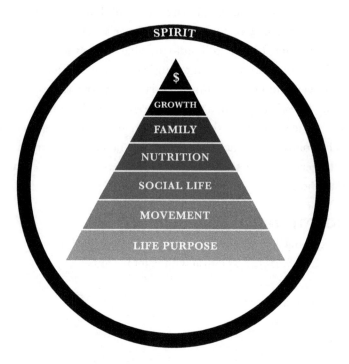

Your longevity or quantity of life is largely determined by three ingredients: your life purpose (career), movement and social life. The quality of your life is most impacted by four ingredients: your nutrition, your family relationships, your growth and your wealth. I call these quality of life enhancers if they are present in your life, or destroyers if they are absent. They may not always add to longevity, but at any age these four ingredients will enrich your life.

There is another essential ingredient, however, and that is spirit. If you avoid putting your spirit – your heart and soul – into each ingredient, your life simply becomes a to-do list of doing the right things, judging your success on your achievements (human *doing*) rather than your fulfilment and who you are as a person (human being).

Exceptional Exercise 0.1: Examine your life

Socrates said "The unexamined life is not worth living." This chapter is an invitation to examine your life in a way you never have before. Begin by taking a moment to look at the following assessment. Identify where you are in each area of life and give yourself a score out of 10 in each ingredient. You'll end up with a maximum score of 80.

Look at the short descriptions and consequences of mediocre and exceptional to generate your score. This is only a snapshot, and by the time you've finished this chapter, the numbers are likely to change.

A word of caution here: some readers mark themselves more harshly than others. Personally, an 8/10 or above is exceptional for me. A score of seven and under feels average to me. Each reader will be different, and I ask you to assess your own life accordingly. Generally speaking, five or six out of 10 is considered to be mediocre. It doesn't feel bad enough to change, yet is nowhere near the life that you want. It's simply average.

Life Purpose – Do what you love and love what you do

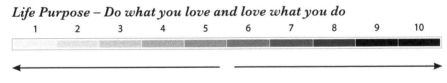

| 1 | 2 | 3 | 4 | 5 | 6 | 7 | 8 | 9 | 10 |

I have a job · · · · · · · · · · · · · · · · · · · I'm on a mission
I don't love my work · · · I love my work (most of the time)
I work to live · I live to work
My work lacks purpose · · · My work fills me with purpose
I can't wait to finish · · · · · · · · I could do this forever

Risk of Mediocre: Regret   **Exceptional Payoff:** Inspired

Movement – To live longer, move more

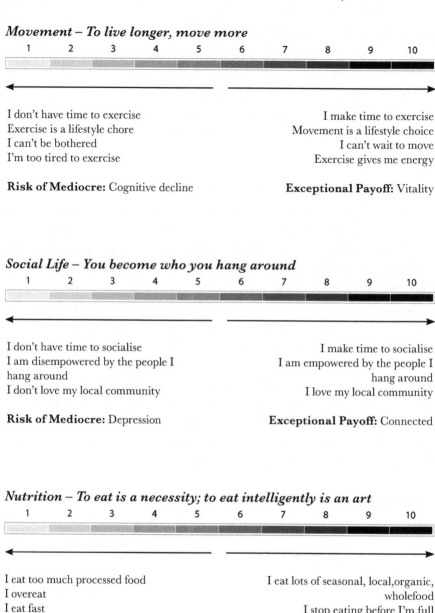

| 1 | 2 | 3 | 4 | 5 | 6 | 7 | 8 | 9 | 10 |

I don't have time to exercise
Exercise is a lifestyle chore
I can't be bothered
I'm too tired to exercise

I make time to exercise
Movement is a lifestyle choice
I can't wait to move
Exercise gives me energy

Risk of Mediocre: Cognitive decline

Exceptional Payoff: Vitality

Social Life – You become who you hang around

| 1 | 2 | 3 | 4 | 5 | 6 | 7 | 8 | 9 | 10 |

I don't have time to socialise
I am disempowered by the people I
hang around
I don't love my local community

I make time to socialise
I am empowered by the people I
hang around
I love my local community

Risk of Mediocre: Depression

Exceptional Payoff: Connected

Nutrition – To eat is a necessity; to eat intelligently is an art

| 1 | 2 | 3 | 4 | 5 | 6 | 7 | 8 | 9 | 10 |

I eat too much processed food
I overeat
I eat fast
I often dine alone

I eat lots of seasonal, local,organic,
wholefood
I stop eating before I'm full
I eat slow
I often dine with others

Risk of Mediocre: Disease

Exceptional Payoff: Energised

Family – Love people for who they are, not what they do or believe

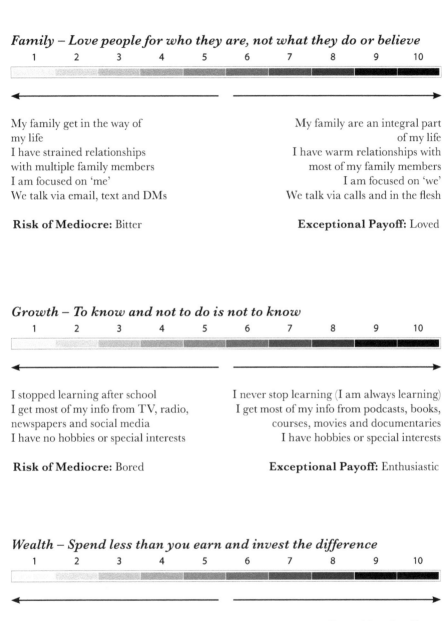

| 1 | 2 | 3 | 4 | 5 | 6 | 7 | 8 | 9 | 10 |

My family get in the way of
my life
I have strained relationships
with multiple family members
I am focused on 'me'
We talk via email, text and DMs

Risk of Mediocre: Bitter

My family are an integral part
of my life
I have warm relationships with
most of my family members
I am focused on 'we'
We talk via calls and in the flesh

Exceptional Payoff: Loved

Growth – To know and not to do is not to know

| 1 | 2 | 3 | 4 | 5 | 6 | 7 | 8 | 9 | 10 |

I stopped learning after school
I get most of my info from TV, radio,
newspapers and social media
I have no hobbies or special interests

Risk of Mediocre: Bored

I never stop learning (I am always learning)
I get most of my info from podcasts, books,
courses, movies and documentaries
I have hobbies or special interests

Exceptional Payoff: Enthusiastic

Wealth – Spend less than you earn and invest the difference

| 1 | 2 | 3 | 4 | 5 | 6 | 7 | 8 | 9 | 10 |

I spend more than I earn
I have nothing to invest
I have no savings
I live pay cheque to pay cheque

Risk of Mediocre: Broke

I spend less than I earn
I invest the difference
I have savings
I have a vision for my wealth

Exceptional Payoff: Independent

Spirit – Everything happens for a reason and a purpose

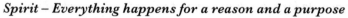

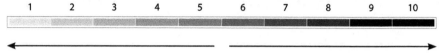

I believe in good and bad, right and wrong, love and hate	I see the bad in the good, the right in the wrong, the hate in the love
I am easily outraged	I can find calm in most situations
I can very easily become narrow-minded	I can see the bigger picture most of the time
I struggle tapping into my intuition	I have a strong sense of intuition

Risk of Mediocre: Broken   **Exceptional Payoff:** Fulfilled

Total
Score   **/80**

SOME KEY HEALTH AND LONGEVITY LESSONS FROM *THE EXCEPTIONALS*

To live longer, move more

Welcome to perhaps the most underrated and misunderstood ingredient for living an *exceptional* life. Whilst most people are feeling guilty or making excuses for not exercising, the longest-lived people around the world are actually... not exercising.

For the *Exceptionals* who are exercising – the 70, 80 and 90-year-old world record holders and Mary, your overactive midweek tennis-playing, garden-loving next-door neighbour whose kids just wish "Mum would slow down" – they are moving in ways they love to move, rather than exercising because they 'should'. They're dancing, swimming, running, playing football, doing yoga, tai chi, horse-riding, cycling, lifting weights, surfing, and so on because they love to, not because they have to. For *The Exceptionals*, movement is a lifestyle choice. For everyone else, movement is a lifestyle chore.

The truth is that less than 20% of the population is sufficiently physically active, and it's causing havoc around the planet. It's even suggested that more than 40% of all dementia would disappear if we moved regularly, and many cancers, diabetes and heart disease all list a lack of movement as a major risk factor.

So what does it take to become an *Exceptional*? Firstly, if 'exercise' feels like a dirty word, replacing it with 'movement' is key. Secondly, know that moving your body becomes more important the older you get. And finally, moving regularly in ways that you love may go a long way to preventing an undignified death.

Enjoy the modern world of technology and at the same time prioritise the time-honoured movements such as gardening or going for a walk to get some fresh air. Exercise because you love to, not because your friend has lost more weight than you.

To ascend from mediocre to magnificent movement, the responsibility is yours and yours alone, and thankfully there are inspirational mentors to help you make it happen. It gives me great pleasure to introduce you to the world of the exceptional movers and shakers.

Transform from Exercise to Movement

"People were so excited, I couldn't get out the front door." An 84-year-old nun was sharing with me how she had become a celebrity in the triathlon world and now everyone wanted a piece of her. "I'm thinking, 'what about the professionals?' They are working their butts off and they aren't getting the publicity they deserve. They deserve the pictures on the front page every day. Instead it's me, this little old lady getting all of the attention."

This little old lady was Sister Madonna Buder, a Roman Catholic nun from Spokane, Washington. Buder had just become the oldest woman in history to complete an Ironman Triathlon when she crossed the line at the 2012 Ironman Canada in under 17 hours. Her rise to fame included becoming a Nike ambassador with her very own television advertisement and being inducted into the USA Triathlon Hall of Fame.

Jan Smith (b. 1944) became the oldest Australian woman to scale Mount Everest when she reached the summit the day after her 68th birthday. The Melbourne grandmother and psychologist started mountaineering when she was 65 and has scaled six of the *Seven Peaks* – the seven highest mountains in the seven continents on the planet.

Accountant Don Riddington (b. 1944), who began swimming when he was 50, became the oldest Australian to cross the English Channel when he conquered the treacherous route at age 68 in 2013.

Nonagenarian Heather Lee (b. 1927) is the world's fastest walker in her age group. Medical doctor Walter Bortz (b. 1930) has completed over 40 marathons. He celebrated his 80th birthday by running the Boston Marathon in 2010. Jack LaLanne (1914–2011), a self-confessed childhood "sugarholic", became host of the first health and fitness television program *The Jack LaLanne Show*. On his 70th birthday he swam for one mile tied to 70 boats.

You're never too old to do anything. Whatever excuses you or others have, there are countless *Exceptionals* who have done what society says cannot or should not be done. Not one *Exceptional* has ever bought into the belief of being too old. Whilst their legs may not be as fast, their mind remains more willing than ever. *The Exceptionals* do not need to be shaken out of bed to go exercise. It isn't a grind. They exercise because they *love* to. For *The Exceptionals*, exercise is not a lifestyle chore; it's a lifestyle choice.

Exercise has been a public health failure

The aforementioned *Exceptionals* who excel at exercise – training for mountaineering, triathlons, sprints and competition – are in the small percentage of people who love to exercise or get enough of it. "Exercise has been an unmitigated public health failure," according to Blue Zones founder, Dan Buettner. "Fewer than 18% of people in the developed world exercise enough. So, it isn't working for the vast majority," Buetnner told Jay Shetty's *On Purpose* podcast. "As we see obesity on the rise in most countries, school kids aren't moving enough. It's (exercise) just not been a successful strategy to deal with our health care problems. It sells a lot of books, it sells gym memberships and gadgets and TV shows and yoga classes. It's a great business, but it's not doing the job, and I feel like the *Emperor's New Clothes* (saying this) – by pointing out (that) it ain't working!

"People think they have to pump iron, run triathlons and break a sweat, but actually walking gives you about 90% of the physical activity of training for a marathon. If you're 80 years old and you can walk a mile (1.6km) in under 17 minutes it adds about six years to your life expectancy. Just the act of walking!"

How much constant and mindless movement do you have in your daily life? Can you – and do you – walk one mile in under 17 minutes on a regular basis? Are you outsourcing a lot of your mindless movement to cleaners, gardeners or using your car or public transport more than you could? Are you succumbing to modern conveniences that easily and unconsciously reduce your daily movement? I'm not suggesting you have to clean your entire house, do all the gardening and sell your car. Instead, consider if you've lost the balance between modern conveniences and incidental movement.

Longevity cultures don't exercise

If the thought of daily exercise has you shuddering, the good news is you don't need to be an exercise junkie to join *The Exceptionals.* "In Blue Zones, people don't exercise – at least not in the way that we think of exercise," Buettner continues. Blue Zones are the locations where people live longer, healthier lives than the rest of the world. "In Blue Zones, people are getting plenty of physical activity into their 90s and 100s because they live in environments that nudge them mindlessly into moving every 20 minutes or so. Every time they go to work, every time they go to a friend's house, every time they go out to eat is an occasion to walk. They don't have a button to push for the housework and kitchen work – they do it by hand. They have gardens out the back. They're in constant, mindless movement which is what I believe we need to start thinking about if we're going to make healthier cities."

On the Japanese island of Okinawa, movement comes from their traditional lifestyle. All Okinawans have a garden they tend to, they eat sitting on the floor – which means they get up and down many times each day – and do a lot of walking. None of it is structured exercise. The Greek island of Ikaria has no gyms or state of the art yoga studios. Instead, they walk and hike the undulating island, swim and body surf in the ocean, dance at their festivals, and tend their land.

In California, the graceful agers of Seventh Day Adventist community Loma Linda are partial to regular exercise, and they also have lifestyle and religious rituals that encourage regular movement. During the Sabbath, Loma Lindans are likely to hike or walk with family and friends on the day of rest and worship. On the Italian island of Sardinia, men living the traditional shepherd lifestyle walk on average eight kilometres per day whilst the women are physically active around the home.

Movement is more important than diet for a long life

"Another gold medal for Australia!" Ruth Frith (b. 1909) had just won one of her six gold medals in athletics at the 2009 World Masters Games in Sydney. Sitting down to do an interview with the ABC shortly after, Frith was asked about her workout routine.

"Monday I do weights, pushups, ride the bike and do some stretching. Tuesday I do that again; Wednesday I do practical training on the field. Thursday I do the same again and Friday I do weights again." Asked if she thought she had an advantage over her competitors because of her workout regime, Frith replied: "Well when I'm with them I find out they don't do anything. A lot of them don't even train!"

When asked her recommendations for movement, Frith insisted: "Even if you only do three days a week. You must, you can't expect to keep going forever doing what you did. I started (athletics) when I was 74. What I did when I was 74 you can't do when you're 84."

Frith wasn't lying; she really did begin her Masters athletics career at 74. Her daughter, Helen Searle, is a Commonwealth Games silver medallist and represented Australia at the 1960 and 1964 Olympic Games, and continued on into Masters athletics when her professional career ended. For years, Frith would go along and mind the bags of Helen and her fellow club members until one day she had her epiphany, as she told me on *100 Not Out*: "Enough of the bag minding, it's my turn to give this a go!"

Frith, who lived to 104, was so exceptional that she won some of her gold medals purely because she was the only competitor in her age group, and she still holds some of the 25 world records she set. Like many centenarians, Frith was regularly asked the perennial question, "What's your secret?" to which she replied, "It's not diet, because I don't eat vegetables. So it doesn't have anything to do with the diet!"

Frith's comments can come across as flippant and some health professionals might be squirming at the idea that movement trumps diet for healthy longevity. However, anecdotal evidence suggests that whilst a great diet is wonderful for improving quality of life and can be a great healing aid, it doesn't contribute to longevity in the same way movement does.

Countless *Exceptionals* have shared with me their daily diet on *100 Not Out*. Lavinia Petrie (b. 1943) runs 10km in 40 minutes on her way to gold medals for Australia. She celebrates with a "hamburger with the lot" and a trip to the bakery.

Sister Madonna Buder is partial to a pastry, whilst octogenarian Ruth Heidrich (b. 1938) is a vegan athlete who's run over 60 marathons and multiple triathlons. Alan and Janette Murray ran 366 marathons in 366 days in barefoot runners, eating nothing but raw fruits and vegetables.

Longevity cultures all have a wholefood-based diet with considerable differences. The Okinawans thrive on rice and fish and consume very few fruits, whereas the Loma Lindans are largely vegetarian or vegan. Corn is the staple of Nicoya, Costa Rica (the South American Blue Zone), whilst the Greek Blue Zone of Ikaria enjoys a Mediterranean diet that differs to the Sardinian version. And of course, Australian Ruth Frith didn't eat vegetables! If you're looking for anything in common food-wise, Blue Zones founder Dan Buettner says the only food all longevity cultures have in common is the consumption of beans. While *The Exceptionals* may not share the same diet, they all have a love of moving their bodies.

I LEARNT THE HARD WAY

Our first child, Maya, was born on January 1, 2010. Shortly after her birth I decided I would complete my first half ironman triathlon in November. Amongst family time and keeping our business running, I began training for the 1.9km swim, 90km bike ride and 21.1km run. Saturday and Sunday mornings were long rides followed by long runs. Weekday mornings and lunch breaks were spent swimming and running, and as a result of the training load, I was tired when I was at home with the family and just wanted to rest.

At a time when life was meant to somewhat simplify (work, sleep, eat and change nappies), life had become unnecessarily complicated. Not only was I tired at home, I was late to most of my training sessions and was cutting it fine with my workload as well. In short, I was overcommitted and I refused to do anything about it or heed the warning signs. On a drizzly Melbourne Cup Day, just two weeks before my half ironman debut, I was on a training ride when a car at an intersection didn't see me coming. It crossed the intersection safely however I was forced to brake, skidded and fell into a gutter, shattering and dislocating my left shoulder.

My overcommitted life was bound to reach a breaking point, and this was it. Amidst the turbulence of becoming a father, supporting Sarah, Maya and our business, I had not only committed to bite off more than I could chew, I had now paid a hefty price for my commitment to being too exceptional. Frustratingly, I had also passed those consequences on to Sarah, Maya and our extended family, who nursed me through two surgeries and the resulting rehabilitation.

In hindsight the stupidity of it all is ridiculous. But sometimes we are blinded in the moment. Even Dr Walter Bortz, who had to stop running at 88 after completing 45 marathons, acknowledged that he put too much focus on exercise. "The Greeks said, 'Everything in moderation' and I was not moderate. I think I just wore (my legs) out, just gone from too much use," Bortz said in an interview in 2018. "I never had any distinction as a runner – I was once interviewed by PBS for coming in last in the Boston Marathon – but I love to run. I'm terribly upset when I see runners running and I can't do it. It bothers me."[33]

Getting the balance right with your exceptional movement is vital. It may take years to discover it, and it may also change overnight. Personally, I completely missed the memo telling me to slow down when Maya was born, instead ramping it up when the opposite was in order. Movement shouldn't be something you're stressing about fitting in. It's akin to worrying you'll be late for a meditation or yoga class; it defeats the purpose.

Unless you're a professional athlete or high-level amateur with a magnificent obsession for competition, your movement shouldn't feel like another appointment you need to get to. Instead, movement is a way of life, a lifestyle choice that can last for hours or just minutes; the type of experience you're grateful to have the privilege to be able to do. Exceptional movement will give you a quality of life nothing else can, and contribute to your longevity more than any other health practice.

> *"If you can only do one thing for your health, remain*
> *physically active. Being active is the life-saver."*
> Stephen Jepson

What then, shall we eat?

There is a disturbing trend in the diet industry. Robert Atkins, founder of the Atkins Diet, died at 72 from a heart attack. Nathan Pritikin, founder of the Pritikin Diet (dubbed "the healthiest diet on earth"), developed two forms of leukemia before committing suicide aged 69.

Michael Montignac, a diet developer who founded the Montignac Diet and influenced the South Beach Diet, died of prostate cancer aged 66.

Adelle Davis, known as 'the most famous nutritionist of the early to mid-20th century', died aged 70 from cancer. Davis claimed it was caused by the junk food she ate in her younger years and a series of x-rays she underwent.

If we are what we eat, surely the diet gurus would be sitting at the top of the longevity ladder? Clearly, life as a human being is more complicated than the food that passes our lips.

We're becoming just like diet experts

This premature death or tunnel-vision on diet is not exclusive to the diet experts. I've observed many people that make their diet too exceptional at the expense of the other key pillars of life.

Visualise this: Mary is eating a pasture-raised open-range chicken salad at her workstation or in the kitchen. It is organic, locally sourced and contains no artificial flavours or preservatives. She is very proud of herself because she is doing the 'right' thing. The diet experts would give Mary a big pat on the back and proclaim she is well on the way to a long and healthy life because 'we are what we eat'. Mary though, also hates her job, rarely moves her body (believing that eating well is more important than moving well), doesn't socialise with her friends because they 'don't understand' her or she has 'no time', and finds herself growing apart from her husband because he 'doesn't understand' her either. The only books she reads are on nutrition, and like most people she spends more than she earns. Her religion is food and she can't understand why people 'don't understand' that. She's right, they're wrong.

Sadly I'm not exaggerating here. Whilst not all elements of that example apply to everyone, our food choices have become an identity that consumes so much of our thoughts that we've lost perspective on what is truly important in life. Drinking green juices, being gluten-free or vegan and eating a strictly organic and biodynamic diet are all wonderful – yet none are the foundation of an exceptional life.

No one diet is the answer

When National Geographic sent Dan Buettner and his team around the planet in search of the world's longest-lived people, they didn't find that one diet fits all. The European Blue Zones of Ikaria and Sardinia eat a Mediterranean diet including vegetables, fruit, herbs, bread, olive oil and wine. Their regular intake of gluten, grains, sugar and alcohol flies in the face of the gluten-free, grain-free and strict vegan diet approaches.

In Loma Linda, California, there is a population of Seventh Day Adventists outliving their countrymen and women and most of the world. Most Loma Lindans are vegetarian, whilst some are strict vegan. Further south, in the Blue Zone of Nicoya, Costa Rica, they subsist largely on corn, eggs, rice, beans, wild fruits and vegetables. In Okinawa their traditional diet includes plenty of rice, fish, tofu, vegetables, and very little fruit.

What these cultures have in common is just as intriguing as what they don't. Moreover, what their diets teach us is that there is no one way of eating that suits the globe's entire population. With that in mind then, the question still remains, what do you eat?

> *"People have to find their own way and then everybody has to*
> *leave everybody else alone with whatever they're doing*
> *because we're all trying to do our best to stay healthy.*
> *For me I do my best being all raw."*
> Mimi Kirk

It's Not All About Your Genes

Mimi Kirk (b. 1939) is my second favourite vegan behind John Robbins. Kirk has been voted the World's Sexiest Vegetarian over 50 (when she was 74) and has been a vegan since her early 30s. When Kirk joined me on *100 Not Out*, she was quick to warn against the danger of buying into the story of family genes.

"I'm the youngest of seven. My mother outlived four of her children," she told me. "My mum lived to be 95, but she was on a lot of prescription drugs. I have an 89-year old sister who takes 18 pills per day, and she's definitely fading. Both of my sisters have cancer. Parkinsons, diabetes and leukemia are in our family, as are high blood pressure, strokes, high cholesterol – everything you can imagine! A lot of these happened at an early age – and I've managed to keep these at bay. A lot of people say 'it's all about the genes'. Well, longevity might be about genes in some way, but some researchers say genes only contribute to 20% of our longevity. (In any case, life) isn't about living long, it's about living well. I might have the longevity gene, but not so much the healthy part of it, so that I have done on my own. I really feel I've manipulated that part so I don't have what my other family members have had."

If you grew up as Mimi Kirk did (in a family that doesn't support an exceptional diet), avoid buying into the belief that you are doomed to live a life of illness. Heed Kirk's example; if you decide to transform your diet, your genes will be in a more supportive environment to fully express their true potential.

Laying your future at the mercy of your genes is not only fatalistic, it robs you of taking any responsibility for your own health. Society will now accept almost any excuse for poor health, genes being one of them. *The Exceptionals*, meanwhile, have mastered the art of eating intelligently by linking their diet to what is most important to them.

DON'T ACT YOUR AGE

MYRNA MANALILI

Y SHIFT

MYRNA MANALILI

These days, Myrna Brabante Manalili understands the importance of good health. However, this wasn't always the case.

Spending most of her adult life in high pressure corporate roles, Myrna's main goal was to be successful by working hard and providing a stable and secure income for her family. For a number of years, this worked well. That was until Myrna found herself struggling to keep her head above water amidst a series of changes to her workplace that coincided with her attaining mature worker status.

Struggling with severe anxiety, stress and other physical health conditions, Myrna found herself at a crossroads. She could stay at her job for a few more years until she reached aged pension age, *or* she could redirect her drive and determination into something that could promote her health and lifestyle goals. Risking it all, Myrna chose to leave her corporate gig and branch out into the health science space, promoting the basic concept of 'Love Your Health'. Myrna believes that we can each take control of our health by gaining awareness around risk factors and making lifestyle changes.

Myrna's experience gives her incredible insight into the various ways work-life balance (or a lack thereof) can impact our health. She understands the nuances within the corporate arena when it comes to mature workers, and how the ageing process is often misconstrued as being innately negative. Her positive outlook on life leaves Myrna with a valuable and relatable perspective on ageing gracefully and the benefits of good physical and mental health for older adults.

Myrna was born in the Philippines and moved with her family to Australia in the year 2000. She holds a bachelor degree in Science and Commerce – Accounting.

You can connect with Myrna at mbmlifestyle@gmail.com, www.myrna_manalili.usana.com, and on Facebook at facebook.com/myrnamanaliliusana.

"The future holds such promise that all the past pales in comparison."
Anonymous

**I dedicate this chapter to my brother
Edgar, Mommy and Pappy who all have
suffered lingering illness before passing on.**

Diabetes, cholesterol issues and now *this:* a knot in my chest, a noise in my head, the headaches, the tight throb running from my shoulders to my ears. It was like living in a pressurised tank – the air too thick and heavy to get to my lungs. Chatter was happening all around me: new computers, staff, and programs. Just when I got the hang of one thing, another was lying in wait to challenge me all over again. Every day was a struggle to keep my head above water in the continual stream of processes that had to be learnt.

What had happened to me? It's not like I always had life so easy, that now with a bit of added pressure, I couldn't help but crumble into a heap. I wasn't weak. I wasn't *fragile.* I had spent my entire adult life working in the corporate space. I knew what I was in for. So, what was with all this *stress*?

THE BEGINNING

I was born in the Philippines, the first of eight children. My father worked while Mother stayed home to care for us. With only one breadwinner for the ten of us, it was tough financially. However, no matter how little money we had, we all managed to get to university and graduate, myself with a Commerce degree majoring in Accounting.

Straight out of university and bright eyed with possibilities, I started my first full-time job in the accounting department of the number one car rental company in the country. I celebrated my first taste of success and making my own money, which allowed me to contribute to raising and supporting the rest of my siblings.

I stayed with that company for a good many years, working in different departments as I found myself itching for varied corporate experiences. It taught me the value of hard work and showed me reward by way of personal growth and improved earning capacity. Of all my workplaces, this is the company I remained with longest.

After getting married, and with a son and a daughter of school age, we migrated to Australia in 2000. It was an easy transition for us, thanks to family who helped us find jobs, a place to settle, and schools for the children.

CORPORATE STATE OF MIND

"Sometimes letting things go is an act of far greater power than defending or hanging on."
Eckhart Tolle – *The Power of Now*

In 2005, I got a new job in a big retail chain. I enjoyed the fresh opportunity: my role was different from previous positions I'd held, as was the nature of the business. It was easy for me to feel inspired, responsible, and committed. I was excited to learn more, to improve and grow. The main office I was assigned to was close to home – it was perfect.

One morning, my manager called me to a meeting room. The department head was already seated, a big smile painting his face. It was good news! They had created a new role for me, which came with a substantial pay increase. Double whammy!

I was truly grateful for their trust and confidence in me. I worked hard to prove myself, mindful of the work ethic that had been ingrained by my first employer.

However, things didn't stay quite so rosy. As I moved into further roles, I found that hard work, discipline, determination, and responsibility required an added layer to be able to perform well – technology.

Though I had the basic technological understanding and skill to get through my work, the emergence of new systems and processes designed to sustain the company's competitive edge in the market greatly challenged me. It wasn't that I was averse to technology or had given up learning new things – I simply struggled to pick it up as quickly as some of my younger colleagues. My long years of working in the corporate world paled in comparison to the incoming young breed of professionals who were already equipped with the tech skills that the workplace demanded.

My desire to fit into the evolving workplace and adapt to new technological systems and processes, combined with my lack of understanding and skills gap, carried a heightened stress and anxiety. I was always on guard, anticipating what was going on around me.

Working in this kind of environment took a significant toll on my physical health. My body ached deeply, though the doctors' clinical tests yielded nothing. I began experiencing chronic headaches, sleepless nights, feelings of lethargy, and extreme nervousness. I could go on to describe the physical symptoms, but it was what was going on in my head that I could not – and still cannot – fully articulate.

What happened at work continues to play like a broken record in my head, no matter the time of day, where I am, or who I am with. As each Sunday rolled around, I dreaded the prospect of heading into the office on Monday. I was sick and scared. I did not feel safe in the environment that was meant to be my comfort zone. The place no longer motivated me; it no longer inspired me. I was not thriving, just (barely) surviving.

Alarmed by my deteriorating health and sanity, I started to consider my alternatives. My kids were all grown up – my son, married and expecting his first child – and so the prospect of becoming a grandma was endearing. I could pick up something casual or part-time to tide me over until retirement age if I wanted to; I no longer needed to spend 40 hours a week chained to a desk. I looked outside of my supposed comfort zone and thought to to myself, *There is definitely more out there, if only I care to look*. With that thought and the fire of anticipation running through me, I decided to leave my job.

LIFE AFTER CORPORATE

"The way I see it, if you want the rainbow, you gotta put up with the rain."
Dolly Parton

It surprised people when I left my corporate job. My peers thought I could have stayed on a few more years and left at the right time. The 'right time' being retirement – a word, a thought, and a future I had not paid attention to or seriously prepared myself for. I procrastinated, thinking it was still far-off into the future. I failed to realise that the day of reckoning would come sooner than I thought, and would in fact be several years earlier than I expected. When the dust settled, I was certain that I no longer wanted to go back to the workforce. But at the same time, I was not ready to settle down into retirement just yet.

Foremost in my mind was to seek medical help for my deteriorating health. I attended various professionals – taking trips to doctors' offices and specialists' clinics. I loved to read books in my younger days, a hobby that took a back seat as I got busier with raising a family. There was a stack I had accumulated over the years that I never got to tackle. I figured I could pick up the hobby again – and I did!

With time on my side, I also thought it would be a good idea to engage in volunteer work. One Sunday at church, they mentioned their need for Special Religious Educators (SRE) for young children in government-run schools, to introduce them to the teachings of the Catholic faith. I thought, "I can do that!" All I needed to do was complete the Catechist Training Course.

I started the program and sat in on classes with an experienced SRE to observe her. It was very inspiring and emotionally rewarding to see these little kids so eager and enthusiastic to learn. You raised a question and the majority of their little hands would be up in the air; the excitement about participating was written all over their faces.

Not long after, I leaned into a company founded on the concept of optimal nutrition for long-term wellness. I was looking for a 'health fix' and this is where I landed. The company's vision was to help people support and maintain their health through the promotion of quality nutritional supplements that worked at a cellular level. Given my experience with health and wellness (and a prior lack thereof), it was easy for me to immerse myself into the company's ethos. It felt like I found my new place and an opportunity to help others live healthier lives.

HEALTH IS TRUE WEALTH

> *"Of all the wisdom I have gained over the years, the most important is the knowledge that health and time are two of humanity's most precious assets."*
> Dr Myron Wentz

We all want to live life to the best it can be. But amid all our wanting to live life to its fullest, a piece of the puzzle is often missing: a lack of attention to our health, stemming from an ignorance toward the risk factors of the food we eat and our lifestyle habits.

Research tells us that degenerative diseases often begin in early years – in childhood![1] – while the long-term effects of poor nutrition and carefree lifestyle habits are manifested later in life. We normally assume the onset of degenerative disease as normal indicators of an ageing person's quality of health. "Well, what do you expect, you're getting old!" is the standard assertion, as if old age justifies the presence of illness.

It is common to find one or two, or even all members of a family, living with one or multiple degenerative illnesses. We could be living with someone who has diabetes, dementia, cardiovascular disease, cancer, chronic knee pain (the list goes on); or, we could be that person living and coping with these diseases.

Life is not fun for people with chronic degenerative diseases, especially if they're taking medication that is causing a side effect, which might require more medication to manage. Further, any medication prescribed is simply to control the aggravation of disease symptoms, rather than a 'cure' of the root cause. The medication is for life because the degenerative disease is for life. It becomes very challenging for family members who look after their sick loved ones, especially for those with deteriorating brain health.

The good news is that there is a lot you can do to help your body fight and better cope with these degenerative diseases. First and foremost, it is imperative to adopt a lifestyle that supports long-term good health.

So, what can you do?

1. **Eat well**

   Eat the best diet you possibly can. It is absolutely essential for long-term good health to know which foods are good for you and which are not. A well-balanced diet supports a healthy immune system. The reality is, the busier we are, the less we care about what is on our plate. Find the time and space to make health-conscious choices. Treat yourself to a healthy meal. Healthy living starts with healthy eating. What you eat makes a difference in how you feel and think. The Healthy Eating Pyramid is still the best guide in the practice of eating basic food, packed with the nutrients we need, on a daily basis.

2. **Supplement your diet**

   The nutrition in our food is declining every year.[2] Farming practices that contribute to agricultural pollution result in soil degradation, causing soil to become too contaminated to support animals and plants effectively. These days, you simply can't get the nutrition you need from food alone.

   To complement your diet, take quality nutritional supplements such as vitamins and minerals. Choose high quality supplements that work at the cellular level. Cellular nutrition means ensuring that every cell of our body

– which is the building block of health – receives all the nutrients needed to perform the cellular function of repairing, regenerating and preventing oxidative damage caused by toxic environments and poor lifestyle habits. Optimal nutrition at the cellular level helps you to feel, think, act and perform your best.

3. Get moving

No matter your age, weight, health, or abilities, encourage yourself to do some form of physical activity every day. Health guidelines require 150 minutes of exercise every week,[3] on top of our normal movement from one place to the next. Ever heard of a runner's high? Well, believe it or not, it's real. When we sweat, we release endorphins, otherwise known as euphoric hormones. Exercise literally pumps our bodies with chemicals that make us feel good. Start at a level that is manageable and gradually build up intensity suited to your capability. Next time you feel stressed, get up and get moving. Even a short walk around the block will give you the space to clear your mind and loosen up your body. Regular exercise will have long-term impacts on the mind's ability to deal with stress, as it stimulates and restores sleep, improves concentration, and betters mood.

THE TRADE OFF

> *"Man sacrifices his health in order to make money.*
> *Then he sacrifices money to recuperate his health."*
> Dalai Lama

I had never been too concerned about my health except when it got me down, or worst case, took me to hospital. Honestly, I only truly acknowledged it if it disrupted my daily life. *A lot of us live like this.* But, as I have come to realise, if we want to enjoy happy and long lives, our health must be actively and regularly considered, not just when we are experiencing illness. We need to give our bodies the best chance to keep us fighting fit if something goes wrong.

Just like everyone else, I needed to work for financial gain to afford a better quality of life, not just for me but for my family. My single focus was to work hard to keep my job, so every other sphere of my life revolved around work.

Working 9 to 5, as Dolly Parton sings, in reality really means working more hours than that – seriously, *what a way to make a living!* During my corporate days, I willingly did more hours than what I was contracted for to reasonably complete my tasks. At times I felt I could use a day off, or that I should call in sick because I was not feeling well. But, as long as I could get myself to the office, I would continue doing my work.

However, there is only so much the human body and mind can endure. It is illogical to run yourself to the ground so badly that you cannot perform at all. But these are the sort of things we do, if only to ensure financial security.

We can recognise the physical impacts of this, but what we don't so readily acknowledge are the impacts that worry and stress have on our long-term health – at least, not until it is too late. In fact, the World Health Organisation (WHO) has dubbed stress the "epidemic of the 21st Century." Research tells us that chronic stress increases inflammation in the body, which can lead to degenerative diseases like high blood pressure and cardiovascular disease (amongst other things). These are serious health issues which put more people at risk of an early death. WHO Director-General Dr Tedros Adhanom Ghebreyesus warned, "No job is worth the risk of stroke or heart disease."[4]

In fact, a 2020 Finnish study found that unbearable stress can shave as much as 2.8 years from an otherwise healthy person's life expectancy.[5] For anyone reading this who has not yet passed middle age, this threat might not seem imminent. But *trust me*, when you get to my age, you will want the guarantee of as many years as you can get.

I have found that after all those years of stressful living, creating 'stress free' moments in daily life is crucial for long-term health and wellness. This may be easier said than done, especially if you have been living and breathing stress for most of your adult life. But here are some science-based strategies I have learnt, that help clear the mind and unplug from everyday drama:

1. Spend time alone

Carve out time to spend alone in a quiet place where there are no distractions. Disconnect from technology and simply 'be' in the present moment. A moment of solitude offers you the chance to remove yourself from thought, turn down the inner noise in your head, and allow for self-reflection. Breathing exercises, done by stepping outside and taking slow mindful breaths while focusing on the scenery around you, will help clear your mind, lift your mood, and reduce stress and anxiety.

2. Be organised

Stress can be a product entirely of our own design. We self-sabotage by procrastinating until we are faced with an insurmountable mountain of tasks to complete. Getting organised ahead of time, setting clear deadlines for when things need to be completed, and mapping realistic steps to get there will save you that last minute scramble. You will be able to see where you can make better use of your time and where you can alleviate some of the strain.

3. Set boundaries

Stress is often caused by us taking on more than we can reasonably handle (such as putting in more hours at work than what is required). Think about what you can manage in a day without becoming overwhelmed. Setting firm boundaries allows you to relax and to feel empowered to care for yourself. Clearly communicate your boundaries as this will set a tone of respect. Of course, sometimes things will come up that you have to deal with – your child gets sick, your car breaks down, a client is in crisis. However, if you have been regularly enforcing boundaries, you will feel more equipped to deal with these 'one-offs' as they arise, as you won't feel burnt out from regularly overcommitting.

Taking the time to recharge and reduce your stress is vital to your everyday mental and physical wellbeing. This is something you can start working on right now!

SOCIAL CONNECTEDNESS

> *"Connection is why we're here. It is what gives*
> *purpose and meaning to our lives."*
> Brene Brown

I'm still married to the same man I met in my younger years – how time flies. We have had our share of the good times and the bad over the years, just like the rest. What I believe got us through, on top of our mutual love, was our respect and understanding of each other. My mother once told me to never entertain the thought of separation or divorce because it's like breathing life into the thought. And I never did. This might explain why he is still my man to this day!

Today, with our kids married and creating families of their own, it's just the two of us. We find ourselves working together in harmony, both recognising the imminent frailties that come with ageing.

We have committed to exercising together by walking – our three-to-four-kilometre walk becomes enjoyable and achievable rather than a hurdle. If my husband turns on the 6 pm news, he'll watch while I cook up a nutritious meal. So that I don't feel left out from the news – and to compensate for his lack of participation in preparing the dinner – he will echo out the headlines (with added commentary, of course). Win-win!

Social isolation is a great risk factor for mortality. A person who is lonely is 50% more likely to die prematurely than a person who has healthy social relationships.[6] Being lonely affects a person's immune system and can cause inflammation which can lead to chronic conditions. Humans as a species can't survive without other people, as we are by nature meant to connect and have meaningful relationships.

In a 75-year-old Harvard study[7] on adult development about 'what makes a good life', the three major lessons learned were:

1. good relationships keep us happier and healthier

2. it's not just the number of friends you have, or if you are committed to a romantic relationship, but the *quality of the relationship*

3. good relationships do not just protect our bodies – they protect our brains as well

When the study was conducted, many of the young people shared common aspirations of fame, wealth, and high achievement because that's what they thought they needed to have a good life. But the Harvard study showed that people who perform the best in life are those who lean into their relationships with family, friends and their community. The study concluded with a clear message that a 'good life' is built on good relationships.

It is not the accumulation of material wealth that matters – it's not about the flashy car you drive, or the investment properties you own. You can't take those things with you to the grave. At the end of the day, what matters most is the love you have for family and the relationships with friends and community that you build through the years. That is the defining quality of a life well lived.

THE 'BONUS' YEARS

"Life is what you make it. Always has been always will be."
Eleanor Roosevelt

People are living longer than ever before, thanks to advances in science and technology, and medical breakthroughs. The United Nations currently estimates a global average life expectancy of 72.6 years.[8] This is significantly higher than in past decades. Babies born today can expect to become a senior citizen – and potentially a centenarian – as compared to past years when mortality rates were much higher.

Baby boomers currently aged 57 to 75 years old will likely live into their eighties, nineties and maybe even into their hundreds: the 'bonus years'. Boomers are gifted more time than they ever thought they had during their young-to-mid adult years. Hobbies, health, and relationships can be given the space they deserve, rather than being forced into a jam-packed schedule.

However, the challenge the ageing population faces today is that most people have not realised they'll have an extra 20 or 30 years after their default retirement age. As such, they are not prepared financially – they don't have sufficient money saved to fund their needs and financial independence in the long term. With age being the most significant factor for chronic disease, baby boomers in their fifties and sixties are in poorer health – 60% are already diagnosed with at least one chronic medical condition, such as arthritis, diabetes, heart disease, obesity, osteoporosis, hypertension or depression.[9]

On a positive note, baby boomers are said to have more money compared to any other generation. Baby boomers have a mental attitude of wanting to stay young and delay retirement. They feel that if they are physically fit, mentally sharp and financially secure, they will continue to be productive and will thrive in their 'bonus years'.

As I've mentioned, the thought of retirement was never there while I was in the corporate world. I now find myself in damage control mode to mitigate the negative impact of not having enough to live on during my own 'bonus years'.

Having said that, awareness is key to having a good life in the long term. With our increased longevity, it is *crucial* to financially prepare so that you can provide the lifestyle you desire for those extra years.

Throughout our lives we plan our family, career, our finances and how to prosper – even our holidays! Financially planning to live our best life in longevity is equally important. We will never enjoy life if we are stressing about where to get money to fund our extended existence.

It is never too late (or too early) to reflect on how you want the rest of your life to be and make sensible and achievable plans. It is in your best interest to be healthy and happy achievers.

While researching this chapter, I read about the FIRE movement. The goal of FIRE is to gain financial independence and retire early through saving and investment. Imagine if you were able to achieve this! Imagine what kind of life you would have in longevity, the many contributions you could make to society, and what you could do to make a difference in the world when you are not worried about money and you have the luxury of time! I only wish I knew then what I know now. But it is never too late to start your journey to having a good life in longevity – take it step by step.

LOVE YOUR HEALTH

"Wrinkles should merely indicate where the smiles have been."
Mark Twain

Have you ever felt fearful of the prospect of ageing? There is so much negativity that surrounds it. With each year that ticks by, we grow more and more afraid of our looming mortality. As a society, we are typically led to believe that elderly people are frail and 'on their last legs'. Older adults experience discrimination and abuse because of their age in the workplace, within families, and in the wider community.

But should we live our extended life fearful that we have gotten old? Do we allow these negative ideas about ageing define how we experience our remaining years of life?

I have found that we have a choice. We can either create and nurture the dream life we choose to live in longevity, *or* we can wallow in self-pity, ruminating over what could have been and how unfortunate it is to be old.

For years, scientists have been examining whether a person's 'subjective age' (whether someone feels younger, the same age, or feels older than they actually are) has an impact on their health in later life. And as it turns out, it does!

In 2018, a study found that a person's subjective age is "closely related to the process of brain ageing."[10] This means that someone who *thinks* that they are younger than their chronological age will also likely *feel* younger. Similarly, studies have shown that there is a direct link between a person's subjective age and their physical health and longevity.[11] So, I guess to say, "You are only as old as you feel" really is more than just a comforting adage! It's a call for action – *don't act your age!*

Imagine this: two people over the age of 70. The first eats healthy food, exercises, is grateful for the experiences and the life they have lived, and embraces their present circumstance. Their age doesn't limit what they can still achieve. They are actively positive and proactive in taking steps to ensure they maintain peak happiness and health.

Now imagine that – instead of thinking and acting positively – the second does the complete opposite. Rather than doing good things for their body and mind, they waste away the hours, complaining about how hard their life has been and feeling sorry for their current state. Who do you think would be happier and healthier? Who do you think would be feeling and looking younger?

There have been many people in this world who were taken too soon, who did not want to go when their time was up, who never got the opportunity to fulfil all their hopes and dreams. This is what I believe: up until the day you die, you have every opportunity still available to you. You can achieve anything you want, go anywhere you choose, and be whoever you want to be. You have been given time on this earth that many others were not so lucky to have, so make it worthwhile!

If you are someone who is resentful about ageing, make a conscious effort to shift your mind to being hopeful about the future. Think about the people you have loved, the family you have cared for, and the friends you have laughed with over the course of your life. Look back on all the experiences you have lived – the foods you have tasted, the books you have read, the art you enjoyed, and the places you travelled. Think about how many new experiences you can still add to these memories. The longer you live, the more you can be, see and do. Be thankful for it.

As it turned out, the significant deterioration in my health over my final years in corporate work was a blessing. Now, I have become more health conscious. I look at what I am eating – not that I was eating all that *badly* before, but it certainly wasn't the correct diet for me. It is important that as we age, we keep on top of good nutrition by eating a plentiful amount of fresh fruit and vegetables, healthy fats, and whole grains. According to Nutrition Australia, other ways we can improve our diet are by consuming more water, less salt, and only a moderate amount of alcohol.[12]

Though initially sceptical, I started taking nutritional supplements and found they improved my energy and outlook, helped me sleep better, and minimised my body's persistent aches and pains. These days, when it comes to flu season, I am spared from it.

I also placed more emphasis on physical activity, drawing inspiration from my children who, despite their busy schedules with work and raising kids, regularly "hit the gym", whether it be at five in the morning or seven at night. So, now my husband and I go for a walk with the dogs on weekdays and longer distance walks on weekends, just the two of us.

Any day is a good day to take control of your health – physical, mental, emotional, social, and financial. Make a commitment to plan a future that may be challenged by degenerative disease. Ensure you work on being cognitively, emotionally and socially healthy. If you decide to look at ageing in a positive light and continue to live life to the fullest, it is almost indisputable that you will be happier and healthier.

Loving your health is your way forward to simply just feeling well.

WHEN YOU BELIEVE

"In the end, it's not the years in your life that count.
It's the life in your years."
Abraham Lincoln

When we think about ageing, we tend to get caught up in what we lose, when instead, we should be focusing on what we have and what we can continue to gain. As mentioned, there is so more out there we can still do if we care to look! By the time we reach old age, we have developed a strong sense of self. We are confident in our identity and no longer crippled by the insecurities of our younger years. We don't care so much about what others think of us – we know who we are and are accepting of that person. We still can reach milestones in longevity as we continually aim to better ourselves.

As we transition into retirement, pick up those dreams that gave way to fears or dream a new dream! Who knows what miracles you can achieve when you believe in yourself unconditionally and you **don't act your age**! Be grateful for every new day!

* * *

Thank You

This chapter is made possible because of two women who
believed in me, even before I believed in myself.

Sarifa Alonto Younes – Author of *Love your Obstacles*
Susan Dean – Dean Publishing

HEALTHY
HYPNOSIS

TANYA LEYSON

TANYA LEYSON

If nutritionist, health coach and hypnotherapist Tanya Leyson is passionate about one thing, it's health. With over 15 years' experience under her belt, Tanya has put her appetite for healthy living to good use – working tirelessly to implement healthy change in individuals, corporates and across society more generally.

It all started as a child on her grandparents' farm. Infatuated by the idea of 'good food', Tanya channelled her passions into cooking and learning what she could about diet and the human body. Since then, she has completed a Bachelor of Nutrition and worked her way through the industry, having gained experience in recipe development, corporate wellness programs and one on one coaching. Tanya has even run her own café and written a cookbook, chock full of her own mouth-watering recipes.

In 2016, Tanya launched The Good Health Coach – a one on one coaching service aimed at guiding and empowering people to better health. Tanya works with clients using a mind and body approach (i.e. while she works on your *physical* health, she is also targeting your *mental* health). By implementing various techniques, including goal setting, accountability tracking and hypnotherapy, Tanya rewires her clients' thinking to not only crush their bad health habits, but to create lasting change.

Living a life of careful design to amplify her own health goals, Tanya doesn't just preach, she practises. What sets Tanya apart are her lived experiences and her understanding that to be *truly* healthy, is to have a lifestyle that benefits you physically, mentally, and spiritually. It is her unique application of nutritional science to the practicalities of everyday life that sets her clients up for success.

You can connect with Tanya at hello@thegoodhealthcoach.com.au and on Instagram @the_good_health_coach.

ONE HEALTH COACH'S MISSION TO HELP AUSSIES TAKE CONTROL OF THEIR DIET.

You wouldn't believe it if I told you. In one day, a full time smoker kicks his lifelong habit. In five, a woman ends her excessive consumption of alcohol. How is this possible?

Let me tell you that though nothing is easy, sometimes things don't have to be as hard as we make them out to be. We each have the autonomy to make lifelong and lasting changes that benefit our health by simply taking small, positive steps toward better habits and behaviour. That first step – the decision to change – is all anyone needs to get the ball rolling. Back it up with the will power and determination to commit to doing things differently, and you are well on your way to a healthier life.

Making a change might seem daunting. The path to get to where you want to go – impossible. Perhaps your goal is to give up alcohol. Maybe you want to lose ten kilos. Your aim might be to banish unhealthy habits, emotional eating, and change relationship with food. Whatever it is that you wish to achieve, I *promise you* it is not insurmountable. In fact, it is easier than you think.

Think about it this way. Changes are occurring all the time, and many of them might feel insignificant. However, even the smallest changes can eventually yield a large impact on the world around us.

Haven't you heard of the butterfly effect? The idea that one small event (the flapping of a butterfly's wings) can have a major bearing on events, even those that may seem unrelated or non-linear (causing a typhoon)? Apply this principle to your health goals. If you change just one small part of your day (adding in a walk after dinner), you will be able to reap huge rewards over time (increased cardiovascular health).

It sounds simple, and it is. However, the problem with us humans is that because we are unable to see every small change as it occurs, we aren't rewarded with instant gratification. This leads to discouragement (or even fear) when trying to tackle a long-term goal. We tend to put off things 'until tomorrow' because we don't see the immediate value in starting today.

Compare your face as it is now to when you were a baby. You are almost unrecognisable, correct? As stark as the difference is, I bet there was no single day, week or even year that you can pinpoint this change occurring. Because (obviously) these changes happened *over time*.

We can all easily understand this concept. After all, no one would expect a toddler to suddenly wake up with the fully formed facial structure of its mother.

Then, how come, when it comes to our own goals, we suddenly forget that change is always happening, regardless of whether we can immediately see it or not? We need to take a step back and think, *if we do this every day for the next five years, where can it lead us?*

I am The Good Health Coach – nutritionist, health educator, cookbook author and hypnotherapist – and I'm here to share forward my story, learnings and teachings to inspire societal change toward a healthier world.

HOW IT STARTED

I grew up in regional South Australia. My mum's family were in agriculture, so as a kid I spent *a lot* of time on farms. I remember watching my grandfather cultivate the land, picking fruit from ripened orchards. He would hand me fresh apricots – each bite filling my small mouth with juicy pulp. Regularly I got to sample the land's labours, perpetually overwhelmed by each harvests' sweet produce.

As I got older, I started to realise that my experience with food was quite unique. Lo and behold, supermarket apricots were nothing like what I had experienced on my grandparents' farm. They were dull and lifeless – a true slap in the face to my family's fruit empire. It was this early exposure to good food that set the foundation for my hobby-turned-career in nutrition.

I was interested in cooking – baking mainly – from a young age and created my own meal plans. I was curious about the ingredients in food and learnt how to interpret nutrition panels so that I could better understand what I was putting into my body. Of course, this was all just for fun – a hobby that I could enjoy in my spare time away from school and chores.

It wasn't until I developed acne at around 14 years old that I really started to take nutrition seriously. My parents took me to a doctor, then a dermatologist, to figure out how to combat the skin condition. I asked both medical practitioners whether my diet had anything to do with the outbreaks. "No," was the reply. Intuitively, I knew that their advice was wrong.

I began doing my own research and discovered that I did in fact need to consume good nutrients to have healthy skin. I reduced the processed food in my diet and eliminated most sugars. Eventually, my skin started to clear up. My overall physical health seemed better too – I felt less tired and my digestion improved.

I was fascinated by the effects that good nutrition could have on my body. So, straight after high school I enrolled in nutrition dietetics at uni. The more I learnt in class, the more notice I took of the food that was available on a societal level, rather than just what was on my own plate. *What were people buying at the supermarket? How did they fuel their bodies?*

Even though I was studying high level nutrition, there were things that weren't really covered in detail or explained in class. What's more, some things just straight out made no sense. Exhibit A was the food pyramid. Back then, the Australian food pyramid was comprised from bottom to top of five to seven servings per day of grain and fibre, two servings each of fruit and vegetables, two servings of meat and a small amount of fats. This meant that the Australian government was telling people to eat *more* carbohydrates than plant based foods. This seemed odd, especially considering that not one of my budding nutritionist peers adhered to these rules.

I checked out the American, Mediterranean and Japanese food pyramids. The Mediterranean featured less grains, placing more emphasis on vegetables, while the Japanese version was different entirely, allowing just one serve of meat per month. Of course, the American pyramid was most similar to our own, though it allowed for a larger number of portions of each category per day.

When I considered the average health of Australians and Americans, compared to that of their Mediterranean and Japanese counterparts, it became obvious that the Australian health pyramid was ineffective at guiding people to eat well. At that time, around 50% of the Australian population was overweight (this statistic has risen to 67% as at 2017–2018)[1] and we were seeing (as we continue to see) a steady increase of health conditions like heart disease and cancer. Conversely, Japan had the lowest obesity rate in the world (and still does)[2] and those who ate Mediterranean diets were consuming anti-inflammatory foods that were high in antioxidants. So, why was our food pyramid built this way?

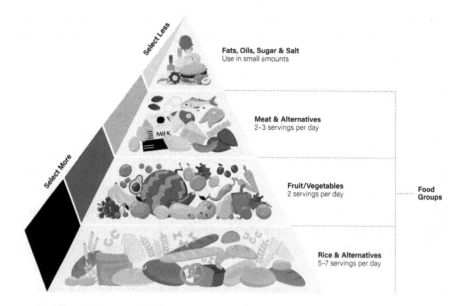

I discovered that the food industry had a big influence on what the food pyramids and guides looked like. The more money put in by a company, the more heavily it was featured. Further, each industry that provided funding had the opportunity to review and approve the pictures that were to be included in the design. For example, the beef industry had to be happy with the icon that represented meat, and the dairy industry had to approve the pictures for milk and cheese.

To say I was shocked would be an understatement. Despite this, I never lost my passion for the industry. In fact, these revelations only made me more determined to learn about the science behind diet so that I could become the best nutritionist possible. I finished my degree, and eventually the Australian food pyramid was changed. As it stands today, the food pyramid and the Australian Guide to Healthy Eating places more emphasis on eating vegetables and fruit, rather than grains and carbohydrates as it once had. *Hooray!*

FOOD IS MEDICINE

After I left university, I started working one-on-one creating meal plans for clients. I spent a lot of time in small companies, health centres and gyms educating people on how to make better nutritional choices.

If there was one thing I learnt throughout these years, it was that what you put into your body, you get out. It was amazing how little people knew about what really went into pre-packaged meals, 'diet' foods, and gym supplements. So many of my clients assumed that their nutrition was fine, but were missing out on essential nutrients and eating too much sugar, and processed and refined foods.

Translating the science behind nutrition and applying it to real people and seeing results was eye opening. What I knew about 'good' and 'bad' food still rang true. But, what I learnt was that every person needed their *own style of eating*. What was working for one person, wasn't necessarily working for another.

I started tailoring my meal plans to reflect my conversations with clients. If someone told me they had any visual cues of poor diet (such as a dull complexion or brittle nails) I would find the root of the problem and adapt their meal plan. This might have meant increasing their intake of vitamins or healthy fats.

As time went on, I started to realise that creating a tailored meal plan was one thing, but getting a client to implement it was quite another. A time-poor client came to me and asked whether I would be prepared to cook and provide her with the ready made meals. I didn't mind so much. However, as more and more clients requested this service, the more unsustainable it became. I was starting to learn that it wasn't *just* the nutritional content of the meals that needed to suit the client, the food also had to satisfy their lifestyle. There was no point creating a meal plan that was impractical for clients to prepare. It had to be tailored to the individual's needs.

I redirected my passion for cooking and started selling my own food at the markets. I met my then business partner and together we opened a gluten, dairy and sugar free shop and cafe. We made our own premium almond milk and veggie burgers, which we eventually sold to other local cafes.

What I loved about cooking was its power to transform everyday produce into something spectacular. Taking whole ingredients and enhancing their flavours through herbs and spices was an art. I was determined to prove that just because a meal was healthy, did not automatically condemn it as *boring*; the challenge of creating something extraordinary from the 'bare minimum' deeply excited me. I wanted my food to tell a story – to be vibrant, flavourful and fun to eat for the palate – while also being kind on the body.

WORKING NINE TO FIVE (OR SIX, SEVEN, OR EIGHT)

After a few years, I ditched the 'freelance life' and decided that it was time to join the daily grind. I started working with food companies full time developing recipes and menus and creating innovative products and nutritional panels. I also worked amongst corporates, rolling out health and wellbeing programs and providing healthy eating initiatives for mining, school and office cafeterias.

The corporate space was an eye opener. I had been so used to working with people who took care of their health, that it was difficult for me to be surrounded by so many harmful food choices. I remember talking to colleagues who were already on coffee number three by 10 am and whose lunch was a greasy takeaway from down the road. I couldn't help but think, *no wonder you are in a bad mood all the time, no wonder you have no energy!*

Poor nutrition was just the tip of the iceberg. The stress that emanated throughout the office was stifling. Sitting on the sixth floor under fluorescent lights for nine hours a day, surrounded by tense peers was a perpetual challenge. Try as I might to protect my own energy, I couldn't help but feel unsettled.

I already knew that health was about more than just exercising and eating well, but what I really started to realise during those years at corporate was just how important having a healthy *mind* was. It became clear to me that there was little worth in focussing on *physical* work, if a person omitted doing any *mental* work.

Think about it. If a person is stressed, they are likely to be experiencing a few different symptoms. They might feel irritable, unmotivated, unfocused or down. And these are just their emotional responses. Stress can also induce physical symptoms like headaches, muscle tension, fatigue and high blood pressure. Regardless of how well a person eats, or how much exercise they undertake, if they are experiencing a prolonged psychological condition like stress, they are not in optimum health. Further, because of the impacts that stress can have on the body, it is unlikely that a person suffering from chronic stress is making the best food and lifestyle choices anyway.

When a person feels stressed, their body releases two hormones: adrenaline and cortisol. While adrenaline triggers a person's fight or flight response via increased heart rate and blood pressure, cortisol increases sugar in the bloodstream and the use of glucose in the brain. Cortisol can also reduce the functions of the immune and digestive systems. The outcome? A stressed person's appetite, particularly for foods that are high in sugars or fats, is increased. Stress can also make a person confuse the signal for thirst as hunger and eat in excess when they aren't even hungry. This can result in unintentional weight gain, which can bring with it a whole plethora of increased health risks (think diabetes, high cholesterol and heart disease).

What I was seeing at work was proof of this. No one had time to consider whether they were 'actually' hungry when they reached for their 3 pm chocolate bar, just like they didn't clear their heads by taking a short walk in lieu of a cigarette break. The constant pressures my colleagues were under programmed them to reach for foods and substances that offered immediate comfort, but didn't do much in the way of creating a healthy existence. In fact, some of their more harmful choices were shedding years off their lives.

This isn't uncommon. As the corporate mentality becomes more ingrained in today's society, with people working longer hours to meet higher demands, stress levels in the average Australian are increasing. Not just that, financial pressures, like the impacts of overarching lockdowns and higher costs of living, as well as familial stressors, have more and more people succumbing to the effects of stress. Have you ever eaten dinner in front of the television to 'unwind' after a tough day of work? You probably found yourself eating faster and heaping more onto your plate than you ordinarily would. This is because, rather than being conscious of your food, you were eating in 'auto pilot'. In a country where the average waistband is growing wider each year, it is crucial that we learn how to manage stress so that it does not lead us to mindless calorie consumption.

Stress related eating is very common, but that doesn't mean we have to *allow* stress to impact the way we eat. Stress affects the way we *feel compelled to eat*, but we can choose to consume foods mindfully instead. Mindful eating is the most effective way to combat stress related eating and its negative effects on diet and health.

So, how can we do this?

• **Keep track of food intake.** Being aware of what meals you have consumed in a day will help you assess whether you want to eat out of necessity, or stress.

For some, having an actual number to look at makes it easier to gauge if there is a legitimate reason to eat. I don't always promote calorie counting, and for some, it can be counterproductive. However, if it does benefit you, there are plenty of free apps, such as MyFitnessPal, that make it very easy to keep track of your calories, macronutrients, and even exercise.

• **Assess hunger.** Are you hungry or just thirsty? Take an objective look at your hunger. Did you eat recently? Have you been engaged in physical activity since you last ate? Do you *actually* feel hungry, or do you just have the urge to eat?

If you are not hungry, find something else to do, like a hobby or productive activity. If you simply *have* to eat in spite of not truly needing to, make sure you have the right options available – this means stocking your home with healthy, fulfilling and nutritious foods.

• **Make healthy choices.** If you are feeling stressed, but it actually is meal time, focus more than ever on eating healthy foods. It is *so easy* to eat poorly during stressful times. Nutrient dense foods will allow your mind and body to deal with stress more effectively. The last thing you need is to put even more stress on your body by eating poorly and becoming sick.

• **Eat slowly.** One of the most effective ways to avoid overeating is to eat slowly – *very slowly*. Take small bites and chew at least 30 times if you have to.

• **Take a drink of water between each bite.** That's water, not juice, soda, or anything else.

• **Eat without distraction.** No radio, chatting, television, cell phone or books. It's just you and your food.

• **Relieve stress in other ways.** If you don't have a legitimate biological need to eat, it's best not to. However, regardless of how strong you are, you will need to deal with the stress that's pushing you to eat. If you don't, you will inevitably give in to food cravings.

Some stress relieving ideas you could try include:
» going for a walk
» reading a book
» participating in a yoga or high energy fitness class
» meditating
» calling a friend or family member
» taking a hot shower or bath

What you put in your body determines what you get out. Feed your body natural food, have a healthy relationship with food, and banish emotional eating. Work with the body and the mind to create the desired outcome.

Now, if there is anything that goes hand in hand with stress, it is being time-poor. And what is one of the first things that gets the axe when we are time poor? Cooking from raw ingredients.

As we become more caught up in our fast paced lives, we grow increasingly accustomed to consuming foods that are quick, easy and accessible. Our mounting obsession with pre-packaged meals and the increasing availability of takeaway options (thank you online food delivery platforms) have left us with little incentive to put in the time preparing nutritious meals from scratch.

But, what are these types of food doing to us long term?

We all know that eating fast food can increase our risk of weight gain and obesity. After all, it doesn't take a rocket scientist to tell you that a diet of double cheeseburgers will eventually force you to go up a size in your favourite jeans. (For some of us, we may even forgo the accompanying fries when we stop to consider the aesthetic implications of the extra calories.) However, what we seemingly forget to turn our minds to are the hidden impacts that takeaway foods can have on our long-term health.

Studies have shown a direct correlation between the consumption of fast food and conditions like heart disease (particularly heart attacks),[3] Type 2 Diabetes,[4] and inflammation, which is comprised in all chronic and autoimmune diseases. In fact, a recent study has found that the number of heart attacks per 100,000 people increased by four for every new fast food outlet that was opened in the Hunter region of New South Wales.[5] These silent killers can be fatal if left untreated, and without regular check-ups, a lot of us are unaware whether we suffer from them until it is too late.

Of course, sometimes the option of ordering take out is all too tempting, especially when cooking after a full day in the office bridges on the impossible. For some of us, we leave our homes before the sun gets up and return well after it has gone to bed. I am not unrealistic. Not every meal we eat will always be prepared with our own two hands.

However, when we forgo the act of cooking, we need to make sure that we choose our alternatives wisely. Almost *every* takeaway joint will have some version of a salad on its menu. Try selecting the healthier option in lieu of fried food, or even just add a fresh side to an otherwise 'unhealthy' option. If we make better informed choices when we do order take out, we can minimise our exposure to hidden chemicals and ingredients, such as processed vegetable fats, refined carbohydrates, sugar and sodium.

FROM NUTRITION TO MY REAL MISSION

As much as I loved nutrition, there was something it was not offering me. I had the information and I knew the science, but telling clients what to eat wasn't enough to instil a healthy lifestyle in them. I needed to break their habits. I needed to find a way that I could mould my clients' behaviours by attacking and rebuilding their beliefs around food and wellness. I needed to go beyond nutrition, I needed to become something more.

I considered my options. *What is the one thing that I need to do, that I'm not doing now, and will help my clients live a healthy life?* I asked myself. The answer was simple: I had to change my clients' mindsets. How could I do that? By expanding my skillset and recalibrating my nutritional expertise into health coaching.

Over the course of the next two years, I worked to obtain my coaching and hypnotherapy certifications. I launched The Good Health Coach in 2016 and saw the difference in my clients almost immediately. My work suddenly became powerful. People who sought me out as a coach were more open to my suggestions than those who had previously engaged me solely as a nutritionist. I suddenly had the influence and the platform to create change in clients' behaviours, and ultimately, their lives.

I began implementing techniques that went above the role of nutritionist. I started by modifying clients' environments – specifically their kitchens and pantries – to better reflect their health goals. Clients could now open their cupboards to healthy snacks and delicious raw goodies, rather than being bombarded with a wall of chip packets and instant noodles as they had done in the past. This idea was so simple, yet completely effective. It didn't just limit each client's access to unhealthy foods, it also served as a helpful visualisation tool to increase their motivation to succeed.

Your fridge and pantry can say a lot about you!
What does yours say about you?

Next, I began focusing on individual goal setting. I worked with each client to map out their goals using the SMART formula. To do this, each target had to be Specific, Measurable, Attainable, Relevant and Time bound.

With this criteria in mind, the first step was to clarify what each client wanted to accomplish, and why. The reason for wanting to achieve the goal needed to ignite determination (for example, losing weight to be able to keep up with the kids, or adhering to a clean diet following a health scare).

We then had to make sure that the goal was *measurable* and *attainable*. I focused on directing my clients' ambitions to those that were realistic. I didn't want to sell my clients short, but I also didn't want to leave them feeling unmotivated if they failed to reach a set target. At the same time, the goal had to be challenging enough that the client would experience growth in trying to succeed by developing new skills, habits, abilities and relationships with food.

The last element was that the goal had to be *time bound*. For each client, we worked together to set a deadline for achieving the goal, to remind and motivate them that it was a priority. Again, we had to make sure that the target was set in reality (while a goal of losing five kilograms might be attainable, it certainly wouldn't be if the deadline was set for one week's time).

Each client was responsible for achieving their goals. Everyone is different, so I workshopped different ways in which they could each hold themselves accountable. This might have included visual cues, like making a vision board, or writing the goal down and sharing it with a friend. I encouraged each client to find an 'accountability partner' so that they had someone to help them stay motivated and share their success with.

It was also important that each client accepted that *no one* (not even me!) is perfect. I wanted my clients to forgive themselves if they made mistakes or did not perform perfectly. This mentality was crucial in ensuring that if a client did experience a minor setback, that it did not derail their whole journey.

The aim of The Good Health Coach was (and still is) not to give clients a rigid diet to follow, but to work with them to create a sustainably healthy lifestyle. The emphasis has always been on making small, simple changes that have lasting reward – shifting the focus from purely nutritional to include physical and psychological health. Every strategy and piece of advice I give is put through the 'busy professional' filter so that even the most time poor clients can benefit from their work with me.

YOU ARE GETTING SLEEPY...

Gary[6] was a normal bloke: he loved his beers and he loved his smokes. In fact, Gary had been smoking for so long it was like second nature to him – that first cigarette in the morning with a coffee to that last drag in the evening before bed. He didn't think about it, he just did it because that's what he always had done.

Eventually, Gary started to notice some things he hadn't paid much attention to before: his breath was shorter, his heart seemed to be beating faster, and no matter how many times he brushed, a yellow stain glossed over his once pearly whites. Gary decided it was time to make a change and kick his habit for good.

Gary tried everything – nicotine patches, going cold turkey – but nothing was working. Eventually, Gary tried something he hadn't thought of before: hypnotherapy.

Now, Gary wasn't sure whether hypnosis would work for him, but he was so committed to taking control of his vice that he was willing to give anything a go. Lo and behold, after just one session, Gary's cigarette cravings had completely vanished. In fact, the following weekend Gary and a bunch of his mates attended a social event. The group of friends spent the evening smoking in the garden shed, but not Gary. He stuck to his guns and didn't so much as flinch when he was offered a cigarette. Gary's desire to smoke had been completely quashed.

I came across hypnotherapy almost by accident. Now, I have always been open to holistic therapies, having dabbled in meditation sessions and chakra workshops most of my adult life. These days, there's a yoga studio on every corner (a pair of yoga pants can go for up to $200 a pop!). But 20 years ago, if you so much as *breathed* a word about spiritual healing, you were automatically dubbed a hippie. Eventually, I decided to introduce hypnotherapy into my coaching practice as another tool that could assist me in breaking down clients' habits.

Now, you know those movies where the hypnotist swings the big gold watch in front of his patient until she falls asleep? Then, when he clicks his fingers, she starts clucking like a chook? Yeah. That's not what I do.

From the moment we are born, we are exposed to different stimuli through the five senses: sight, sound, smell, taste and touch. When we experience something new, our mind concocts a narrative around it and decides whether it is 'good' or 'bad'. Sometimes, we form these opinions subconsciously. Once an opinion is formed, it is reflected in our behaviour. Our behaviour determines who we are, which in turn, leads to outcomes.

For example, a child is told that they must eat everything on their plate before leaving the dinner table. Because of this, the child forms the opinion that having any food left over after a meal is 'bad'. The child learns to consume everything that is on their plate, even if they are full, because to not do this would be wrong. This behaviour is repeated over and over and carried into adulthood. The adult now consistently overeats, leading to unhealthy habits and weight gain.

Now, let's say this person wants to lose weight. No matter what they eat or how often they exercise, nothing seems to be working. They eventually realise that it's the *volume* of food that they are eating – not out of hunger, but out of habit – that is the cause of the problem.

Simple, they think. *I will only eat when I am hungry, and stop when I am full.*

The problem? Once a habit has been ingrained, it is a lot harder than anticipated to break. In the above scenario, the individual would find it exceedingly difficult to portion control, cease eating when full (especially if the meal is 'not finished'), and identify legitimate hunger. (You would be surprised how easy it is for the mind to trick us into thinking we're hungry once we are in the habit of 'eating a certain amount at a certain time'.)

This is where hypnotherapy comes in.

Hypnotherapy involves working with and tapping into the subconscious mind. During a session, the client is put into a 'trance state'. This is a deep state of relaxation, where the client's brainwaves are more active (i.e., the point just before they fall asleep). Once the client is in the trance state, they are more open to suggestions. The hypnotherapist (me) can then speak to the subconscious mind about the particular habit that has been formed and the beliefs that trigger the actions around it.

Sometimes, the hypnotherapist will need to work with an emotion that is attached to the habit. (Using the above example, an emotion connected with the habit of overeating might be guilt or stress, derived from childhood experiences.) By using verbal repetition to disassociate the emotion from the habit, the hypnotherapist can shift the client's mindset.

Hypnotherapy can be used to assist with a variety of health issues including anxiety, addiction, stress and pain. However, hypnotherapy will only be of use to those who *genuinely* want to create change in their lives. For example, if deep down, you don't *really* want to stop drinking, then no amount of hypnotherapy will help you quit!

It is also important that the client supplements hypnotherapy with a conscious effort to break the habit. Again, if you are using hypnotherapy to lose weight, but aren't striving to exercise or eat better, then it is not going to be of much benefit!

MY LIFE, MY ADVICE

The thing about becoming a coach is that you do a lot of the work on yourself as well. Through my own learning, I have discovered who I am and what I really want. I have decided to design my own life.

I have now left Adelaide, the city I had spent my entire life living in, and moved to Melbourne, into a house right near the beach.

These days, I wake up and take a stroll by the water's edge every morning. I put my headphones in and listen to music or a podcast about health and wellbeing or business. It gets me into the right headspace and inspires me for the day ahead.

Eventually, I return home. Depending on the day, I will either prepare for my first coaching session or consult (which I either conduct online or in an office a few suburbs over from my home). I spend my days working on my terms and in my ideal environment. There is no long commute, no tense office pressure. I use the extra time and space to fill my day with the things that make me truly happy and healthy. At the end of the day, I take a long walk or run, absorbing my beautiful surroundings.

I shop at local markets and buy organic where available, avoiding potentially harmful sprays and pesticides, which can be carcinogenic, may contribute to Alzheimer's disease, and can affect hormones and the endocrine system. I only buy meat that has been raised as naturally as possible. The quality of the food we eat is so important. It is something that I promote with clients, and pay close attention to in my own life.

Use food, exercise, water, sun, supplementation and relaxation to heal and nourish the body.

I am healthy because of my lifestyle, and I have an amazing lifestyle because I am healthy. I really have built a life I can be proud of.

I think this is what makes me a good coach. A lot of my clients are trying to make radical changes in their lives. It is daunting! It would be easy for them to simply give up, to accept 'that's the way things are' and not strive for better.

But they don't. And what helps them is that they are guided by someone who has made some *drastic* changes in her own life – a person who truly understands how difficult and important it is to engineer your own health and happiness.

If you want my advice, to make your health a priority you must first value it, and then put time and effort into sustaining it. But, it will be near impossible to do this if 'living healthy' is at odds with your lifestyle. Your lifestyle needs to be *conducive to* your health goals.

Think about what your 'vice' is and what is causing it. For example, do you frequently overindulge in unhealthy foods and substances? Why do you do this? Is it because you are stressed? If so, what can you change in your life to reduce your stress levels? These are the things you need to consider and work on when trying to live a sustainably healthy life. There is no point putting strict health rules in place if they are unrealistic and unattainable. Once you design a life that truly makes you happy, you will be surprised how easily your health falls in check. (Think of it this way, no one living the 'rock star lifestyle' is eating acai bowls and practising yoga everyday!)

Get to know your body and pay attention to it. I know what I am prone to. When I feel something coming on, I start taking action *before* it becomes a problem. Deal with the smallest symptom as it comes up, before you have to treat a larger condition.

This isn't just in regard to your physical health. Your emotional, mental and spiritual health are just important when it comes to nipping issues in the bud. There is no way that you can have optimum physical health, if your mental health is suffering.

Don't let a symptom turn into a disease.

To take control of your health means to take control of your habits, your choices and your behaviour. All it takes is one small step to make lifelong change. Are you up for it?

"HEALTH IS THE
SOUL THAT
ANIMATES ALL
THE ENJOYMENTS
OF LIFE, WHICH
FADE AND
ARE TASTELESS
WITHOUT IT."

– SENECA –

FIND YOUR
SPOT IN LIFE

MONIQUE SARUP

SHIFT

MONIQUE SARUP

No matter the situation or what life has thrown at you, everyone deserves to love themselves and live with true purpose and passion.

As a Mindset Coach for youth and young adults, Monique's mission is to help women dare to create the life of their dreams. Monique assists her clients in realising their true potential through goal exploration and works with them in mapping out practical steps to reach targets. Supporting her clients every step of the way, Monique believes that no dream is insurmountable – it's just about uncovering the right path to get there. She understands the pressures and challenges that face young people today and helps them 'find their spot' in life and the world.

Using leading-edge, self-development techniques and personalised coaching methods, Monique helps young people gain confidence, self-esteem, and life skills so that they can move forward in a direction that fulfils and motivates them. Monique empowers her clients to live life on their terms, providing them with the skills to manage and overcome hurdles as they arise.

Having commenced her own self-development journey at the age of nine, Monique understands the importance of young people understanding their minds, emotions, and unique purpose in life. Monique has 'walked the talk', and actions her own advice and mindset techniques in her day-to-day life.

Monique's coaching sessions have often been described as both 'fun' and 'life-changing', and that's exactly what she sets out to do – change lives, without compromising on the good stuff.

Monique lives in Mount Macedon with her husband Sanjay and their daughter Zara. You can connect with Monique monique@moniquerene.com.au

REALISE YOUR DREAMS THROUGH MENTAL GROWTH

It might sound unbelievable, but my personal development journey began when I was just nine years old. I was introduced to self-development quite early due to my parents believing that self-education is key to living your best life. At the time, my sister attended with me, we were in a room filled with over a hundred other kids aged between 8 – 12. At first, we thought it was just going to be a bit of fun, like a school camp, but we soon found out it was going to be an eye-opening experience for the next few days.

We had grown up in a happy home – free of trauma, violence, and neglect. This might sound pretty normal, but at this course, we were surrounded by people who had – in their short, young lives – lived through some truly awful stuff. There were kids dealing with divorced parents, kids who had endured abuse, kids who truly didn't know what it meant to grow up feeling safe and secure and loved. We felt incredibly lucky, and were amazed at how the leaders of the program helped these kids go from anger and sadness, to feeling happy and empowered. It was just incredible to see first-hand.

Being life coaches, Mum and Dad had raised us in an environment that encouraged and nurtured personal development. I even attended the 'Unleash the Power Within Youth Leadership Program' when I was just 12 and was blown away when Tony Robbins himself grabbed my hand as I walked across the embers of fire in one of his well-known firewalking ceremonies.

What I didn't realise back then was that this was somewhat 'out of the norm' for a lot of families. I had no idea that other people didn't grow up with these same opportunities, that they may not know about self-care and growth. To me, it was common sense.

I guess, at the crux of it, I didn't understand how I was supposed to implement tools for mental health when I already felt mentally healthy. I hadn't had to deal with anything that came even close to what some of my peers had. So, how was the course relevant to me?

Looking back, it was from this course that I learnt you don't have to be struggling with mental health to work on it. Skills around healing and managing trauma are of benefit to everyone. In fact, by learning how to implement healthy coping techniques when you are well, leaves you more prepared and resilient when you aren't. Mental health is something you can work on every single day, and like training a muscle at the gym, or learning a new skill at school – you will get stronger the more you develop it.

I slowly started to realise that the people who didn't have an education, a family, or a loving home, *of course* weren't going to be focused on acquiring self-development tools. No wonder they didn't know how to work on their mental health – they were in survival mode, just getting through the days, weeks, and months – one step at a time.

Something ignited within. I couldn't exactly articulate what it was just yet, but intrinsically, I knew that I wanted to help others. Maybe it was seeing the transformation of these unhappy kids who arrived on the first day and turned into amazingly happy confident kids after working with the leaders. Now it was me who was seeking out more ways to grow and learn so I could help not only myself, but others too. I gradually immersed myself into the personal development world as an ongoing journey.

FINDING MY SPOT

The years rolled on and high school came around. It was a heavily science-focused school, which meant that a lot of my friends ended up pursuing fields that were science-based. There were career-based counsellors that were focused on university-based careers: lawyers, doctors and engineers. I wasn't interested in any of these types of careers so it was hard to envisage my future career, other than the fact I was always intrigued by psychology and human behaviour.

After high school, I took a gap year. I was passionate about knowledge and wanted to experience what the world had to offer. So, I jumped on a plane on my own and headed over to the U.S.A to learn from some of the best trainers in the world. I was only 18 at the time and didn't have much to my name, bar my determination to learn. I applied and was accepted into a training program with Dr. John Gray (American counsellor, lecturer and more commonly known from his authored book *Men are from Mars, Women are from Venus*). This was a life and business coach training program that taught you proven skills and techniques to help people in relationships, not just personal ones but in careers and business relationships too.

Doing this course cemented my passion and desire. I wanted to dedicate my life to empowering others by teaching them the skills and tools to live happy and healthy lives, filled with passion and purpose.

When I returned to Australia, I got my first coaching client. She had just started high school and needed a little guidance around school struggles, family life, friend dynamics, those sorts of things. This resonated with me – her problems were easy to talk through because of my own learning and upbringing. Whenever she had a dilemma, I knew exactly which tool to implement. Together, we worked on her mindset, exploring basic techniques like affirmation repetition and breathing exercises. It was incredibly fulfilling sharing forward my knowledge and passion.

But it wasn't all fun and games. My return to Australia also meant a return to the real world. I hadn't established a permanent coaching business, so I enrolled in university and decided to focus my education towards business. My parents had always run their own businesses and I saw first-hand the benefits of being self-employed, so I wanted to invest in my education and later obtained a bachelor degree in commerce.

After completing my degree, rather than just jumping into working with my parents in their coaching business, I decided to go it alone and work outside the family business to get my own experience. I began a full-time 9 to 5 job and – surprise, surprise – it was a shock. I was used to working casual hours throughout school and study where I would go to my shifts and leave without a worry. I had to leave for work at 7 am, just to sit in traffic for *hours* every day, it was not the way I was brought up. I quickly learnt that owning a business was very different to working in one. I loved the people I worked with but the industry was built around a rigid hierarchy. I was running myself ragged trying to work my way up the corporate ladder. The reality of my job was completely different to how I had imagined it.

After growing up with two entrepreneurial parents and watching them run their own businesses, doing what they loved, I was inspired to do the same.

I desperately wanted to coach, to do something that made a difference and gave back to society. So, I committed to becoming the best in this field and making it my passion.

* * *

My mother was a great role model for this, she had a business she loved which involved helping others publish their stories and knowledge in a book, she coached and she had the benefits of being her own boss. So I asked to join the family business and use the skills I had gained from my college degree to help grow the company whilst also being able to grow my own coaching business. I too was now doing everything I loved: being in the education field, coaching, *and* growing my own business. I now coach women aged 13 to 30, using the skills I grew up with, studied, and researched, to help them improve their mindsets and better manage their day-to-day struggles. I find that many of my clients are striving to be and do more, but they don't have a clear path. My job is to get them from where they are, to where they want to go, with clear direction.

Dreaming and Doing

How often do you set a goal, or have an idea in your mind, that you never write down or map out? I provide my clients with a pathway to achieve their goals by working out how to connect the steps between A and B. Together, we find a route that is achievable. I believe anyone can do anything – even if the goal seems insurmountable, it is always possible.

I had a client who dreamt of going to the Olympics. From the get-go, she knew what she wanted – to be an athletic superstar. Now, what do you think was getting in her way of making progress toward that goal? Was it that her dream was unrealistic? Or, that she didn't have the drive and commitment to put in the work? No! The roadblock was her deep-seeded belief that she would never get there! So, she aimed for other, more achievable targets instead, that did nothing to progress her real long-term dream.

Together, we broke down her goal into small, achievable steps – she could do it; we just needed a map to get there. We talked about how we could get her to the level she needed to be at to make the Olympic team by setting a clear plan of how she could work training in with her studies – setting up morning routines and daily goals and affirmations, keeping her accountable, and encouraging her that her dream *was* achievable.

COACHING WITH PRESENCE

I wanted to become a coach to spread awareness and educate others about mental health. There is so much information out there – online, on TV, across social media – about having a healthy body, but a lot of Western medicine is so focused on your physical state, that it omits to consider your mental one.

These days, mental health is getting a lot more recognition. But back when I started out on my coaching journey, it wasn't a big thing. There weren't a lot of resources about being mentally healthy and using your mindset to achieve goals.

Psychologists often focus on the past, delving deep into patients' memories and experiences to teach them how to better understand themselves and heal from unresolved trauma. Coaching is different. My focus is on the future and using mindset to get a client to where they want to be. If issues from the past are brought to the surface, then *of course* we will discuss and work through them. But as a coach, that is not my primary objective.

There is absolutely a time and place for psychologists; I think they're fantastic. However, there's also a need for professionals who sit in the 'middle ground' – people who can offer advice to those who want to grow without first having to heal from the past. There are so many women out there, especially in the 13 to 30 age range, who want to advance their mental health and improve their day-to-day lives. They're not necessarily struggling with big life hurdles, but they want to do the work.

When I was growing up, there wasn't really a space for me to learn about mindset and mental health because nothing was 'wrong' with me. Many of my clients are in the same boat. They've grown up in supportive environments and have never been exposed to any great traumas. However, they are stuck in a mindset of anxiety and depression, perpetually wondering why they are struggling because life has been great. They don't want to see a psychologist or counsellor, but are eager to learn how to better implement mental health strategies.

One of my clients Abby shared an experience she had been subjected to – this experience not only had a profound impact on her, but it also had a profound impact on the way I work with my clients.

Abby had just recently moved out of her parents' home and felt a bit lost in her life. She didn't really know what she wanted. So she decided to make an appointment with a counsellor to help her navigate her crossroads in life (this was before we had met and started working together). Abby went to her appointment full of hope and started divulging her fears and insecurities to the counsellor. About halfway through the session, the counsellor *yawned*. Abby instantly felt invalidated and tears filled her eyes. She couldn't even speak. She felt the counsellor was just 'going through the motions' of therapy – she was there but not present. She was doing the attendance but not the attitude. Abby felt rejected and could sense the counsellor was just getting through her session without any emotional investment or care. She didn't seem interested in Abby's pain or willing to help her transform her life. Abby left deflated but somehow determined not to give up.

So she found another coach, an influencer with thousands of Instagram followers. Abby said that overall the coach was great, but she'd never forget their last session together. Abby had told this coach about the 'yawn incident' in their first meeting together and explained in great detail how that experience had made her feel – invalidated, frustrated, distressed. She told the coach "It scared me into never wanting to see another counsellor again!" Then, during their last appointment, this coach was *scrolling on her phone.* Abby's feelings resurfaced and the old wound of not being heard or validated ripped open. Abby simply couldn't believe it. She decided to never let herself be vulnerable again. And swore she'd never go to another counsellor or therapist.

It wasn't until Abby and I met through mutual friends that she trusted me enough to share her experience and we began working together.

Hearing Abby's struggle to be heard made me even more passionate about being completely present during every single one of my coaching sessions. To always ensure that I am giving my all to the women who take the brave step of asking for help. As author and psychologist Dr Marshall Rosenberg said, "Your presence is the most precious gift you can give to another human being."

I live by the statement. Sadly, a lot of people in the personal development and self-help industries are driven by money or prestige rather than making a difference. Or they don't live and breathe the personal advice they give to others. As a coach, I believe you need to be congruent and practice what you preach. It doesn't mean you'll always get it right, but your integrity is vital.

I guess these experiences continue to frustrate me because I know how much effort I put into my clients, not only during our sessions, but around the clock. A lot of coaches will just attend to a client for the hour that they're with them, have a chat and collect their fee. I work with people 24 hours a day, seven days a week. I am *always* on call. If my client rings me at 3 am on a Sunday, crying in the shower, you best believe I'm going to answer.

I've seen many coaches who work a strict 9 to 5 and when 5 pm comes along, they swiftly tuck their coaching phones away, only restarting them come nine o'clock Monday morning. But when you're going through shit, you don't go through it during business hours. You can struggle at any time of the day or night.

Although I totally understand work-life balance, I also believe this can be done whilst still attending to your clients' needs. It's all about your *why*; that's the real driving force.

Yes, I help women achieve their goals and get to where they want to be, but a big part of what I do is navigating life's hurdles. It's not always about focusing on targets and deconstructing how we're going to get there.

Sometimes someone has a shitty week because their boss isn't treating them well, or they've just broken up with their partner. During that time, we're not going to focus on the path to an end goal. In that moment, we are going to move through what they're struggling with. Coaching is about giving clients the tools to deal with anything that comes up in life. I don't want my clients to need to depend on me for the rest of their lives, I want them to walk away knowing how to navigate life and how to implement the things we work through. When a client begins to answer their own questions and work through their own hurdles during our sessions together, I know they are ready to either set bigger goals or navigate life without me as their coach. Both are winning options to me.

THE STRUGGLES OF YOUNG ADULTHOOD

The fact that you were born into this world is literally a miracle – the odds are about 1 in 400 trillion, or more! Now add in the fact that you were born into a privileged country, where you live with a roof over your head, food in the fridge, and clothes on your back. You have access to education and health resources. You are more fortunate than over 80% of the world's population!

We are so lucky, yet some individuals remain completely miserable.

I believe that everyone was placed on this earth purposefully. Like a game, the journey of life is to find your spot and the reason why you are where you are, have been where you've been, and are heading towards where you are destined to go. The prize? Well, that's up to you.

Being a young adult should be a time filled with fun, excitement, memory making, and self-discovery. However, many of us find these years challenging, confusing, and emotional. This can be extremely difficult, not only for the individual, but also for their friends and family.

We all wish for the brightest futures, but unfortunately people often get sucked into a life of limited self-love, broken relationships, and stifled ambition. We become disillusioned with our lives because we have begun our journey to adulthood without knowing how we fit into the world.

I believe these feelings of confusion and uncertainty stem from our earliest experiences. Let's take school, for example. So much of the education system is focused on maths and science and doesn't offer much in the way of opportunity for students who are creative or artistically minded to practise what they love. Some subjects, like music and art, allow *some* room for creativity, but are still highly structured. If you want to be a dancer, actor, musician or entrepreneur, there's not really space to pursue these fields within the traditional schooling system. Trying to navigate an institutional setting that doesn't nurture your natural talent can be hard.

The pressure of trying to fit into this mould is then compounded once the young person leaves high school. They are suddenly faced with the biggest question of all: *what are you going to do with your life?* After 13 years of rigid schooling, this is a lot of pressure to place on someone, and often leads to many young people jumping straight into tertiary education, without understanding where their true passion lies.

So, they go to uni and waste their money, thinking it might be a good idea. (Of course, university can be great – as long as you are passionate about what you choose to study.) Then they join the workforce, and that's a struggle too. They enter a field they are not passionate about, simply because they spent all that time and money on study; to not put their degree to use would 'be a waste'. Fast-forward to adulthood and they are anxious and depressed because they haven't found their spot in life!

My mission is to help these young people discover their spot – their *why*. Why they get up in the morning, why they do what they do. Your why is your purpose, your reason for being and doing. Whether that is deciding to pursue university, or discovering that uni isn't the only option, is all part of the journey.

I want to give people the tools so that they can create the life of their dreams. No matter the situation or what life has thrown at you, everyone deserves to love themselves and live with true purpose and passion. I want women to know their worth and become the best versions of themselves. Not everyone will love you (or even like you), but there is a spot for *everyone* in this world. With the right guidance and understanding, I believe we can all find it. If you are grateful for and love where you are at, and where you have been, then you have found your spot!

Another huge challenge that young people face is managing social media. It is at the forefront of our lives and is one of those things where if you're not on it, you're missing out. But then if you are on it, you're also opening yourself up to the difficulties it poses, such as missing out on the physical aspects of socialising, which are incredibly important for young people.

Social media can place overwhelming expectations and pressure on youths to act, look and think a certain way. It provides a constant stream of comparison, leaving users feeling inadequate if they don't measure up to others on their feeds.

What a lot of young people don't realise is that much of what is displayed on social media is not reality – it is simply a highlight reel of what people *want* to share. It does not capture the bad days, the struggles, or the failures. Social media provides an edited and curated snippet of peoples' lives – it does not paint a complete picture.

Then there are the influencers – the people whose *job* it is to look good. They have the 'perfect' body because their product is their image, just like they have an impeccable wardrobe because they get paid to promote the clothes that are sent to them. I'm not against social media, particularly using it to make a living, but it is *undeniable* that constant exposure to it can leave young people feeling inadequate – like they will never be as beautiful/rich/successful/happy as the person looking back at them from behind the phone screen.

FINDING BEAUTY IN THE MUNDANE

Self-development is essential for everyone. Once you finish school and start working, particularly in a 9 to 5 situation, life can become very routine. The weeks become a blur – every day is the same, on repeat. You start completing tasks on autopilot – driving down particular roads, or past certain buildings, on the way to work become the norm. You stop noticing the little things around you because they are always there. Life becomes an unrelenting series of Groundhog Days.

Anxiety is fear of the future, and depression is fear of the past. Many people struggle to live in the present, and instead focus on where they have come from, or what's around the corner, rather than what is right in front of them. How many times do you drive down the same road, or ride the bus along the same street, and one day discover a big tree, or a beautiful house that you hadn't seen before? By not living in the present, we miss out on some of the amazing things life has to offer.

For me, personal development is about getting out of that routine and trying to grow every day. I wake up each morning in my house and take the time to notice everything around me. I acknowledge all the things that I have worked for and achieved. When I drive down the same streets that I see every day, I don't ignore them. I look at the trees, the buildings, and the people. I am grateful for all that life has to offer, and mindful in everything I do.

If you live like a zombie, you're not growing. Take time every day to soak in the world around you. Notice the little things – the smell of your toast cooking in the morning, the steam that rises from your coffee. There is beauty in everything. Once you start living consciously, you will find the small moments that inspire you to keep putting in the work.

Think about whether there are any small changes you can make to your week to mix things up. Is there a different route you can take to work, or a new coffee shop you could try? Incorporating some fresh experiences into the mundane will help break you out of that mid-week funk and add some spark to your day.

DOING THE REAL WORK

Working on your mental health is not a one-stop shop. Think of it like physical fitness – you can't just focus on it momentarily, lose some weight, and expect that the muscles will remain. You need to continue working on it, forever, to keep fit, moving and healthy.

Mental health isn't something that you work on once and is 'fixed'. It involves constant commitment. To develop a healthy mindset, it is important that you implement daily and weekly routines and strategies that you can build on over time. It isn't just a 'self-care day' or 'some alone time'; the work needs to be done every day, week, month and year, for your entire life. This can be difficult, but it is worth it.

1. **Love yourself**

   Self-love is going to be ground zero in your self-development journey. If you don't love yourself, you will struggle to grow – there are no two ways about it. Think about it, how are you going to regularly show up for yourself if you don't think you are worth it?

   There are no quick fixes when it comes to improving self-love, but there are a number of techniques you can implement that will, over time, help increase your feelings of worth. This may include repeating affirmations, cutting out negative self-talk, and practising empathy toward yourself. It might sound silly, but by simply being nice to yourself, you will notice a shift in your self-esteem.

   We often don't realise how harmful we can be to ourselves. Even I fall into this trap – I might speak poorly about my body or criticise my intelligence. We are all human! But, it should come as no surprise that continuously doing this can have a sustained negative impact on your mindset. Thinking negatively about yourself will only breed further negativity into your life, directly impacting your overall happiness.

You need to love yourself before you can love anyone else. This is something I have learnt, both in life and in relationships. If you are constantly picking on yourself and are unhappy when you are alone, then you are not going to be your true, full self around others. You need to remove your masks and love who you are, so that you can give your all in relationships.

2. Implement a healthy lifestyle

Step two is going to be the basics – exercise, diet, and water. Instilling a healthy lifestyle will do wonders for your mindset and give you the physical foundation to be your best self. If you are not eating nutritiously, exercising regularly, or drinking enough water, then that's what you need to work on before trying anything else. There are people out there popping ten pills a day to manage their mental health. If you need medication and it works for you, then I support that. But, medication will only take you so far. If you are not living a healthy lifestyle, then you will never reap the full benefits of pharmacotherapy.

3. Practise positivity

Practising positivity is another fundamental step in maintaining a healthy mindset. Like speaking kindly to ourselves, we need to make a conscious effort to view life from a positive perspective. This will ensure that every day is filled with as much joy as possible. For example, if something doesn't go your way and you think, "This day is crap," chances are that you are going to continue having a crappy day. However, if you respond with something like, "That was unfortunate, how can I turn it around?" you will be more likely to pick yourself up and move on.

This doesn't mean you can't get angry, upset, or bored when something doesn't go right – no one expects you to be positive 100% of the time. But, by choosing optimism over pessimism, you will enhance your overall quality of life and increase your level of happiness.

Sometimes when we are down in the dumps, that is where we want to stay. We want to hide in our little bubble of sorrow and self-pity and wallow. There is nothing wrong with this. In fact, sometimes it is better to sit with our negativity so that we can fully realise and process our emotions. However, if you are unable to break out of a negative frame of mind but *want* to shift it, then it is important to learn the techniques around how to do that.

One example is anchoring. Anchoring is a great technique that can assist you in shifting into a positive mentality by attaching a specific emotion to a stimulus (AKA the anchor).

To create an anchoring technique, every time you feel healthy or happy, do an action. For example, you might have a win at work and flick the hairband on your wrist. Now, the flicking of the hairband is anchored to a feeling of happiness. The next time you are feeling down, flick the hairband and your mind will release the positivity it associates with that action.

4. Manifest your life

I manifest *religiously* and it works every time. I'm only 26, and last year my partner and I put together a clear vision board of what we wanted to achieve over the next five years.

Guess what! Within a year and a half, we had literally ticked everything off! We knew what we wanted, stuck photos above our sock drawer, and looked at them every day. There are still a few things we want for our future, but as far as a house, a family, and getting married, we have achieved it (to the point that we've actually got the weatherboard house in the same paint colour that we had pasted on our board). We've had our baby. I was also really sick in 2019, so I manifested good health – which I can now also tick off. All of that happened because of manifesting.

WORKING WITH EMOTIONS

From a young age we are told that 'boys don't cry', to 'stop being a sook', and that 'there are bigger problems in the world'. Sentiments like this encourage us to ignore our instincts that tell us to sit in our feelings and analyse where they are stemming from. I know, for myself, that I often push negative emotions down to convince myself that life is perfect. I try and focus on the good, when what I am really feeling is the bad. I think that by pushing those feelings away, they will disappear. But it doesn't really work that way.

Feelings are like a punctured car tyre that is clunking along the road. You can forget it is there and hope it will go away, just like you can put tape over it and pray it will cover the hole and be alright. *Or* you can acknowledge it, think about what is happening, and come up with a solution – like the spare tyre in the boot.

Although I have the know-how around how to manage emotions and I like to look on the bright side of life, I still have moments where I feel down.

Sometimes I need a cry, or an 'off day' to then wake up and start fresh.

Because I know a lot about personal development, sometimes I feel as though I'm not allowed to have these negative emotions. I can't help but think that if you are teaching something, you should have your shit under control at all times and be able to manoeuvre out of any negative emotions.

But, just like I tell my clients – emotions are there to be felt, and they aren't always pretty. Sitting in your emotions and feeling them, without questioning or having a reason for them, is a true skill. If your negative feelings last more than 24 hours, or happen often, then *of course*, you should try to understand the root of the problem and how you can move past it. A deep-seeded issue may require your attention, or professional support. But, if it's just an off day, know that it won't last forever. Most of the time, there is no specific reason as to why you are feeling these emotions. Just let them pass.

It isn't in our genetics to ignore how we are feeling. And believe it or not, negative emotions can sometimes be a *good thing*.

Let's take anxiety, for example. By definition, anxiety is the "distress or uneasiness of [the] mind caused by apprehension of danger…"[1] – its purpose is to keep us safe and out of harm's way. Anxiety presents itself via the signals of fear – whether expressed in the form of a racing heart, sweaty palms, or shallow breathing – and is the body's way of alerting us that danger is present. Anxiety is what stops us from walking carelessly onto a busy road or running into a paddock of wild animals at night.

Anxiety fills us with fear so that we have the time and space to decide whether what we are doing is correct. However, sometimes this alert system can run amuck.

Anxiety only becomes problematic when there is no 'real' danger to be wary of – we might invent a scary scenario in our mind, or catastrophise an outcome that has no real prospect of occurring. If you are experiencing this type of anxiety, it is important to analyse where the fear is stemming from. Perhaps you are nervous about an upcoming social event, or worried about a presentation you have to give at work. Dig deep to uncover *why* you are afraid of these things so that you can proactively and appropriately deal with it.

FINDING A TRUE COACHING CONNECTION

Working with a professional who is up-to-date and constantly on the lookout for new and innovative ways to work alongside today's society is a great starting point when beginning your personal development journey. Once you have found that special person, you will need to implement the skills and tools they give you as you level up and move through life. The most beneficial way to work on your mental health will involve sustained learning, research, and training. Growth may feel uncomfortable, but you have to stop walking in the same spot, for a new path to appear.

If you are a parent who feels stuck and helpless when it comes to your child's struggles, or if you feel like you have little influence and input in their life, then your first step is to find someone who can act as a mentor and role model for your teen. On the other hand, if you yourself need guidance and support, you should start by seeking a mentor who can help you feel heard. Find someone you truly connect with and are drawn to, to help you begin your self-development journey.

A coach can be incredibly helpful when it comes to learning about mental health, mindset, and self-development – like a tutor for schoolwork, or a personal trainer for exercise. Personally, I think mental health support is absolutely necessary for everybody, regardless of whether or not they are experiencing hardship. Our minds are the most important things we have, but sometimes, we neglect providing them with the stimulation they need. How often do we seek out professional help for our physical health – a doctor for pain, a dentist for cavities, a nutritionist for diet? We are constantly trying to learn and grow and heal in every aspect of our lives but ignore seeking the support that helps us improve our mindset. This work is essential.

In an ideal world, everyone would start learning about mindset from an early age. When I coach clients who are just starting out on their personal development journeys in their late twenties or early thirties, I can't help but think how much time they have lost not working on their mental health. Of course, it's never too late to start doing the work, but why not reap the benefits as early as possible?

We assume that children automatically learn everything at school, failing to realise that they need help with mindset too. Educating children on mental health sets the foundation for them to develop strength and resilience, and will encourage them to be open when it comes to their own psychological wellbeing. This means that they will be more likely to seek help when they need it. This is important for parents to know, because they can encourage their kids to work on their mindset and assist them in finding a coach.

When seeking to engage a coach, the most important thing to look for is connection. They should be someone who makes you feel comfortable in opening up and speaking honestly. Aim to work with someone who has created their own path, and can hold your hand while you build yours. They should act as a role model, of sorts. Any coach that you consider engaging must have already worked on their own development.

When finding a coach, look for someone who is congruent. There are business coaches out there who say they can make you a million dollars, but they haven't done it themselves; just like there are life coaches who claim to know how to maintain a positive mindset, but don't actually implement the techniques they preach. When I engage a coach, I look for someone who inspires me – someone I admire because of their own self-development journey. Choose a coach who you look up to and aspire to be like, someone who is consistent in everything they say and do. You want someone who walks the talk.

THREE PIECES OF ADVICE FOR HEALTH AND HAPPINESS

If I could give every young person three pieces of advice for their happiness and health, they would be:

1. Don't rely on others to make you happy! Happiness always starts with you.

2. Getting outdoors and breathing in fresh air, drinking plenty of water, moving your body and eating nutritional food, are the simplest ways you can work on your mental (and physical) health.

3. There are 24 hours in every day. If you cannot find one hour to be with or work on yourself, you have a problem. We spend so much time with others that we often forget about ourselves. You need to allocate dedicated time for yourself EVERY. DAMN. DAY.

"THE HUMAN BODY
IS THE BEST
PICTURE OF
THE HUMAN SOUL."

– TONY ROBBINS –

RECOVERING WITH RELATIONSHIPS

ROBERT HALL

ROBERT HALL

If you had to spend 540 days (and counting) strapped to a hospital bed, what would you do?

You might cry, you might complain, you might think life is unfair. You might even believe that the universe is out to get you.

Not Rob.

After experiencing a fall that changed life as he knew it, Rob Hall has spent most of the past two years in hospital, remaining optimistic while doctors work furiously to save his leg. Without a prognosis, Rob continues to play the waiting game.

According to Rob, it is his support system that has gotten him through the dark times. Rob was diagnosed with post-traumatic stress disorder (or post-traumatic *growth*, as he likes to call it); a product of the accident and the years of treatment that has ensued. Taking it in his stride, the man who "never used to cry" has discovered that opening up to mental health treatment proves invaluable when it comes to dealing with the psychological effects of injury.

Rob is indebted to his personal supports, particularly his wife Michelle, who have stood by him every step of the way.

Rob began his career as a jockey at just 14 years old, racing competitively for many years until a fall from his horse rendered him unable to continue. He then pivoted into real estate, a career he loves due to its focus on networking and building relationships. Rob has dedicated much of his life to volunteer work and has spent the last 20 years with Country Fire Authority.

You can connect with Rob at robert.hall@gisborne.rh.com.au.

"It's okay to be a glowstick: sometimes we have to break before we shine."
Jadah Sellner

I remember the feeling of riding; air whipping through me as we glided around the track. Hunched over her back, legs glued at her sides, together we'd fly – past the pressed suits and flutes of champagne – cheers rising as dust kicked up from her hoofs. Adrenaline pumped through us both as we charged down the course, as if she and I were one.

Sometimes we won and sometimes we didn't. But what never changed was that feeling – the feeling of flying, of being invincible – like nothing else mattered except you and your horse.

Now, as I spend my 540th day (and counting) in a hospital bed, it seems like a lifetime ago.

Growing up, I always wanted to be a jockey. From the age of three I would go down to the stables with Dad in the cold, dark hours of the morning. It was exhilarating, being awake while the rest of the world slept. Dad would hold me up to stroke the gentle giants, their heads as big as dinosaurs.

A few years later, I started school. Though this institutional inconvenience put a halt to my early morning stable visits Monday through Friday, I'd still be up there every weekend helping Dad wherever I could. I loved it – the atmosphere, the people, the animals. It was my home.

By the time I was 13, I was riding trackwork and got my licence riding races the following year. School was not a priority for me. Racing was. Lucky for me, my parents supported my decision to race full-time. At just 14 years old I was granted an exemption from school so that I could chase my dreams.

Riding competitively was thrilling. I started out in the smaller races and worked my way up to the bigger ones. I was fierce. My edge was that I could push until I had nothing left – forcing myself and my horse to perform to our absolute limits. Winning was the only thing on my mind.

As my years racing began to accumulate, so too did my injuries. The first was a fall from my pony Snowy into a brick wall. I was in hospital for two weeks and spent four days in a coma. When I came out, I couldn't talk. Mum was absolutely beside herself but didn't give up in trying to coax the words out of me. Eventually, I responded, and a while after that, was on the mend.

A few years after the Snowy fall, I fractured my wrist racing. This seemed to set in motion a chain reaction of accidents and injuries. Over the next 15 years, I endured many trackwork falls and a few more race ones. I believe I was unconscious 11 times.

The worst of them was an incident I had up in Bedourie. When I was 17, I was asked to compete at the annual Birdsville races, a weekend event which then went on to become a circuit of southern Queensland. I figured it would be a great opportunity, not only to race, but to see parts of Australia I never had before.

I had a horse come down on top of me, straight onto my left femur. It was fractured, and I was taken directly to Townsville for emergency surgery. I recovered, but my leg was never really the same.

I continued to work in the industry for quite a while after that, though I didn't compete. I started as a Foreman for my dad who trained at Flemington, moving onto part time Barrier Attendant, then Assistant Starter, and, eventually, Starter. By that time, it was my job to start the races from the barriers. Basically, I was the guy who had to make sure that everything went according to plan – that the races ran on time and were conducted safely.

One day when I was down at Seymour, I jumped from the barriers and landed the wrong way – right on top of my ankle. I was in *excruciating* pain and taken straight to hospital, which is where I remained for the following eight months. (Little did I know that this would be just the first of many long-term hospital stays.)

I developed a condition called post-traumatic focal dystonia which made the entire right side of my body spasm uncontrollably. I underwent multiple operations with no success. Eventually, the doctors decided that the best course of action would be to amputate my right leg at the knee.

Now, I was still a young bloke at this stage. There was no way I was going to let them chop off my leg! So, they went to Mum, hoping she'd sign off on the procedure. "It'll get Rob out of hospital; it'll stop the spasms!" they said. Luckily, she told them the same as I did – "No way."

Eight months went by, and I was eventually released from hospital. Then came the real struggle – the eight long years of physio and hobbling around on crutches. I eventually got walking again and continued working at Racing Victoria, this time in the office.

As grateful as I was to Racing Victoria for keeping me on (they truly were an incredible bunch), the office life just wasn't for me. I wanted to be hands on with the animals – to be out in the fresh air, in the thick of it. I didn't want to be stuck at a desk all day filling out paperwork. That's when I got into real estate.

It was a great pivot. I was out and about, talking to people and making connections. I loved the networking part of the job – growing my social circle and building trust. It wasn't really about the sales, they were almost ancillary. In my mind, the most important aspect of my role was to develop an honest rapport with every client. (After all, what person would leave the keys to their biggest asset with some guy they didn't trust!)

THE DAY THAT CHANGED MY LIFE

16 August 2019. As if my brain has been stamped with a branding iron, the date will be etched into my memory forever.

It had started out a good day (as all days where something goes horribly wrong usually do). Early morning appointment at one of my listings, an appraisal of a friend's house, and a visit to a new property, which I then listed later that day. My wife rang me and said she'd cook a lamb roast for tea (Michelle doesn't cook, which should have been my first indication that something wasn't quite right in the universe) and then I negotiated a sale of a house that was scheduled for auction the next Saturday. Everything seemed good in the world. As the last order of business for the day, I arranged a meeting with the vendors of the property I'd just sold.

I drove to their place, parked, and crossed the road. I was met by a wide paved driveway that led to a modern and airy family home. 'Lifestyle + Luxury' we'd captioned it on the website. I'd only just begun the slight descent when, *smack*, my feet slipped out from under me and I fell flat on my bum. It seemed minor enough, much like falling over on a wet bathroom floor or pool tile.

But, the triviality was short-lived, as pain seared through my body. Fire tore up my limbs as I sat alone on the cement, unable to move. If the pain wasn't enough to send me reeling, the sight was. My leg was facing the wrong way and looking back at me.

I screamed out, convinced no one would hear me. *I'm going to be stuck here until someone walks past, and who knows how long that will be!* the grim thought sending me into panic. Then, by some miracle, the garage door rolled up and out walked the vendor. '000' he punched into the phone.

RELATIONSHIPS WITH PROFESSIONAL SUPPORTS

"Fall seven times, stand up eight."

I was never one to cry. That sweet and salty discharge had not wet my cheeks in years. It wasn't that I was emotionally stunted or particularly adverse to crying – I just don't think I ever had anything *really* worth tearing up over.

Well, let me tell you – I am no longer a stranger to the waterworks.

After the fall, I was taken straight to emergency and operated on – I'd broken the head of the femur. "The worst fracture I've ever seen," I believe was the sentiment of my surgeon. From there, I spent five weeks in rehab, before being sent home.

I kept working with the physio, but something wasn't right – after three long months I still couldn't lift my leg at all. Back into hospital I went, this time for a total knee replacement.

How I wish that was the end of it. But it was just the beginning.

It was this operation that precipitated my next two years of hell – of endless hospital admissions, operations, infections and complications. Of immeasurable pain. Of missed milestones, family events, and time with friends. Of loneliness. Of fear. During the next 24 months, there were times that I wanted to die – the pain so excruciating that I thought I was being burnt alive from the inside out. Then there were the times that I wanted to give up – the mental torment almost outweighing the physical.

The first time I cried was like an avalanche. The emotion poured out of me, flooding my eyes as I sat breathless. I was shocked, to say the least. *I don't cry,* and yet, there I was – eyes stinging, nose running, lungs heaving – unable to control myself.

This opened the floodgates, so to speak. I was suddenly crying every chance I got – talking to Michelle, chatting with the nurses. I even cried in Harvey Norman!

After my first 'outburst', the hospital referred me to a psychologist. Ordinarily, I would not have agreed to this – I don't talk about my feelings and prefer to keep things bound up inside. But, I guess I was vulnerable and they thought I needed a chat. I don't remember her name, but as soon as we started talking, I broke down – a blubbering mess of emotion gushed out of me. I could not believe it. Back then, 'it's good to cry', was certainly not a sentiment I wanted to buy into.

I continued seeing the psych, and surprisingly found it comforting opening up to someone. As difficult as it was, I began to place more and more trust in my new confidant. I felt a little better having someone I could talk to, as if a weight had suddenly been lifted.

Eventually, I was sent home from hospital. The psych said she would continue to see me, despite no longer being an inpatient. That suited me just fine – I didn't want to restart the process of getting to know someone from scratch, and the last thing I wanted was to attend a local therapist and have the whole town knowing my business.

Then, one day, I received an A4 envelope from the hospital. Expecting it to be paperwork, I opened it without a second's thought.

Well, it wasn't from the hospital, but a letter from my psychologist, saying that she could not continue working with me. I was no longer a multi-therapy patient and did not meet the requirements for treatment at the hospital.

I was pissed off. She had won my trust and all I got was a lousy letter saying she quit on me. Not even a phone call. I felt abandoned and alone. What was the point of therapy if they just threw you to the wayside the first chance they got?

Without psychological help, the wild bouts of crying continued. Almost anything would set me off. I went back into hospital and eventually started seeing another therapist, but didn't really make a connection. I think I trialled three before I finally got it right.

Eventually, I met my current psychologist, Stephen Rendall, and psychiatrist, Dr Sarah Farrand. Once I settled in with them, the progress I made in my mental health was *incredible*. Their support transformed my recovery journey, providing invaluable relief to the endless months I spent confined to my hospital bed. My eyes were opened to the psychiatric impacts of my condition – apparently, I was suffering from post-traumatic stress disorder (a name I *hate* – post-traumatic *growth* describes it much better) – which explained many of the symptoms I was exhibiting.

Together, we explored various techniques that assisted in the management of my mental health. This included Eye Movement Desensitisation and Reprocessing therapy (EMDR), progressive muscle relaxation (PMR), and sound healing.

1. EMDR

   We started by wading through the murky waters of my mind using **EMDR** therapy. This is a technique that involves harnessing and reprogramming a patient's reaction to traumatic memories and images. EMDR is widely used in PTSD treatment, but can also be helpful in treating anxiety, depression and obsessive-compulsive disorder.

   Through **EMDR**, I discovered that my mind is *filled* with memories that I haven't dealt with – feelings that have been left to fester beneath the surface. This is a commonality in all of us, not just those who experience post-traumatic growth (like me). Everyone must heal their unresolved traumas before they are able to fully tackle their current problems. When you start this journey, you will be surprised what you uncover.

2. PMR

   We then explored PMR. PMR can be effective in minimising stress and anxiety through the grounding of the body with mindfulness. For me, PMR had the added advantage of assisting me in my pain management. Anyone can practise PMR, and the benefits are multifaceted.

   To start, sit, stand, or lie down. Remove all distractions, if possible. (Keep in mind that PMR can be practised anywhere. So, if you are usually stressed in the office, you might find that completing the exercise at your desk is of most benefit. In that case, disturbances may be unavoidable.)

   Begin with the first group of muscles. Tense these muscles and hold the pressure for about five to ten seconds. For example, if you start with your face, you will begin by scrunching your eyes, eyebrows, and forehead, pursing your lips, and clenching your jaw. After the time has lapsed, release and relax. Slowly breathe in and out for a few seconds before moving onto the next muscle group. Repeat as you work your way down the body.

3. Healing through sound

   Implementing sound was extremely beneficial in my healing process. I have heard wonderful things about meditation, but it's just not for me. However, what I do enjoy – something that offers me great comfort – is listening to meditation music and podcasts about pain and healing. I have found myself zoning out to the calming tunes or becoming inspired through others' advice and stories throughout my time in hospital.

If I could offer one piece of advice, it would be to not discount the benefits of mental health treatment – or any medical treatment, for that matter. (In fact, in conjunction with Stephen and Sarah's support, these past two years would not have been bearable without the incredible team of medical staff who helped me get through the physical repercussions of my injury. The pain, which at times was so agonising that I wanted to end my life, was expertly managed. My doctors and nurses truly did whatever they could to ease my discomfort.)

Don't assume that help isn't for you. As someone who was absolutely *hellbent* on keeping things bottled up, I really believe that talking to someone (especially an external and impartial third party) is of extreme benefit. Put in the effort to find a therapist, psychologist, counsellor, coach – whatever – that you can connect and work with. Even if you have to trial multiple professionals, like I did, it is worth it.

There is help out there. Don't be afraid to ask for it. There are many people, programs and treatment options available that you can engage with and lean on. There is no point suffering alone.

RELATIONSHIPS WITH PERSONAL SUPPORTS

> *"Being deeply loved by someone gives you strength,*
> *while loving someone deeply gives you courage."*
> Lao Tzu

The first time I had one of the dreams I thought I was going crazy. I woke – sitting bolt upright – shaking and covered in sweat. I couldn't remember what had taken place in the dream, but I was petrified. Waking up trembling and staring at the ceiling, unable to work out where the ground was and which way I was facing – whether I was up or down – was truly terrifying. It was something I'd never experienced before. I had heard about nightmares like this and seen them in movies, but didn't think they happened in real life.

The nightmares continued as time went on. In many of them, my late father would appear. Others would be filled with old friends, family homes, and places from my past. In a particularly frightening one, I remember my legs were in the air and the ground opened up beneath me. They were tremendously vivid at the time.

The dreams made me wary of sleep. For four and a half months I feared closing my eyes, succumbing to unconsciousness only when my body could no longer stave it off. Even then, I'd only get about three or four hours shut eye.

I didn't tell the nurses, but instead let it fester and grow, until sleep became something I truly dreaded. Then, something changed.

I had made a friend during one of my many hospital stays. He was going through something comparable to me physically, was a strong 'man's man' – a big, tough Aussie ocker guy – and was experiencing similar emotional problems to what I was. He was also receiving treatment from Sarah.

I reached out to him and told him about the nightmares – something I wouldn't ordinarily do. I was desperate. I needed help and I wasn't sure where to turn. We were in his ward talking when he said, "Rob, I get them too." I couldn't believe it. This whole time I had been thinking that I was mad! Though I didn't wish the experience on anyone, least of all a friend, it provided indescribable comfort to know that I wasn't alone. In fact, he later said that talking to me helped him get through his mental health struggles, too.

He told me to talk to Sarah about the nightmares, because she had helped him in dealing with his. It was in that moment that I truly realised there was help out there – help that I previously wouldn't even look at. I had an incredible personal and professional support network all around me, all I had to do was lean on them.

One of my biggest problems back then was not asking for help. I have a wonderful family, beautiful friends, and exceptional co-workers – but I did not want to depend on any of them. I did not want to be a burden. I felt so bad for all of them, for having to deal with me.

In fact, when I was at my worst, I told Michelle to leave me – to go and find someone else. I told her that I couldn't fight the pain any longer, that she'd be better off moving on. She could be happy that way.

But, of course (and thank god) she didn't. She was immovable. My rock. My shelter in the storm, my angel. Everything she could possibly give, she gave. Through the ups, the downs, and everything in between, she was there – stoic and still smiling.

I am a very lucky man. Where would I be without her? Where would I be without my family, or these great people that we call our friends? I could not and still cannot believe all the support I have been given.

I remember the countless times my sisters would drop everything just to be at my bedside; how Mum would regularly bring me sandwiches; how my kids, nieces and nephews would cheer me up with handmade cards and gifts; how my friends would travel for miles just to pop in, even on Christmas day. I remember the countless messages of support, from close friends and those from afar. All of that just for me. I really am blessed.

RELATIONSHIP WITH SELF

Without the support of friends, family, and medical professionals, I would not have survived these past two years. Sure, I'm still in hospital. But am I alive? Yes. That's something to be grateful for and an achievement I could not have attained without my team of people standing right beside me.

But, for all my external supports, there is one internal relationship that I need to maintain if I am ever going to make it out of this hospital bed – one person I have to keep stimulated and inspired and positive. Me.

I am the one who has to sit alone with my thoughts when the nurses have gone to bed, just like I'm the one who has to accept and make the best of my current situation when I get out of here. There is only so much other people can do for me. I need to make sure that my relationship with me is strong enough to pull me out of the dark times, so that I make it to the good ones.

Healthy body, healthy mind

When you ask me what the hardest part of this ordeal has been (and continues to be), my answer is, *undoubtedly*, "being away from Michelle." There are no two ways about it – that has been the absolute pits. But, one other – perhaps comparatively minor set-back – has been not being able to use the gym.

Now, the gym hasn't *always* been a big part of my life. Sure, I had the odd membership here and there over the years – the spits and spurts that we all do. But, it was about five years ago that I decided, "Rob, enough is enough – you aren't getting any younger! It's about time you got into shape." I joined a new gym, and it was unlike any other I had been a part of. The trainers were all about the individual. Not only did they tailor programs around my fitness goals, they became involved in nutrition as well.

Since then, the gym became an integral part of my day-to-day. It is my self-care. Remember how I said I don't meditate? Well, that's because, for me, the gym fills that role. It is my outlet to switch off and go completely crazy. Before the accident, I would be down in the gym at 5:30 am, five days a week, sweating it out for 45 minutes.

Of course, when you're strapped to a hospital bed, the gym is just about the last place you are going to be venturing off to. But, it is still possible to engage in physical activity, even in such a restrictive situation.

During my last long stint in hospital, I had a small dumbbell set at my bedside. This allowed me to complete repetitive upper body exercises, such as curls, bench presses, and chest flyes, all from bed. Whilst this kept me physically fit, it also helped keep me *mentally* fit. This is vital for someone going through a long and painful recovery process.

If you are recovering from an accident, undertaking exercise – whether it be lifting a five-kilo weight, stretching your muscles, or simply practising arm and leg lifts from your bed – will help you in the long run. Movement can have a *massive* impact on recovery, as it can aid your body in mending itself. In my case, all the doctors had commented that my physical well-being was a great help in my early recovery stages.

What's more, engaging in regular exercise while incapacitated will give your mind the stimulation it needs to assist your body's recovery. Setting yourself small daily movement goals will give you something to look forward to and aim for. This can prove invaluable when the fatigue and monotony of long-term admission sets in. Even if your target is to complete just a small number of reps per day, once you tick it off, the dopamine hit will give you an instant feeling of satisfaction. What's more, the endorphins that your body releases through exercise will help keep your spirits high and mind positive.

You don't need to be a gym junkie, like I was. But, you do need to get your body moving, even if for just a short amount of time every day. Make it fun; make it something that works for you.

What's on your plate?

If there's one thing that goes hand in hand with exercise, it's nutrition. Eating a wholesome and balanced diet will feed your body the nutrients it needs to stay fit and strong. Eating well is of benefit to everybody, but especially to those who are in recovery. When you are recuperating, you need to give your body the best opportunity to heal and regain strength.

When in hospital, eating well and drinking enough water is vital to the recovery process. Becoming malnourished or dehydrated may result in muscle loss, fatigue, or significant weight fluctuation. All of these things may impinge your healing.

At home, we have a big veggie garden. There is nothing better than walking out the back (when I'm not stuck in here!) and grabbing a couple of caps and a stalk of celery to cook with. The produce is crisp and fresh, and the smell of it sautéing in the pan is absolutely mouth-watering. Not only that, home grown veg packs so much more flavour than the processed foods and stale produce you get at the shops.

I encourage everyone to try and grow their own produce, where they can. Incorporating just a few potted herbs into your outdoor space will bring life to your home cooked meals and will actually incentivise you to get into the kitchen.

Also, using home grown fruit and veg might actually save you money. How often do you fork out for wilted herbs from Woolies, only to throw half the bunch away the next day? Having crops to hand will give you the chance to pick only what you need, when you need it, thereby cutting your waste and cost.

Of course, not everyone has the space, time, or inclination to maintain a veggie patch. If you would rather stick to buying, rather than growing your food, focus on purchasing organic or farm direct produce. That way you will still get the best nutritional value from your ingredients.

Attitude for gratitude

Never underestimate the value of positive thinking when it comes to healing your body and maintaining your health. Consciously choosing to see the bright side will not only promote feelings of happiness and joy, but will give you the mental energy to complete tasks and remain productive. This motivation is crucial when it comes to health. In a general sense, the more motivated we are, the more likely we will be to eat well, exercise and practise healthy coping strategies. When it comes to recovery, if we are motivated, we will be more inclined to implement treatment recommendations, and channel our energy into healing, rather than wasting it on negative thoughts.

Of course, there have been times that I have felt so low that I just wanted to end it all. *Of course*, I have had moments of complete despair – where I felt like my world was crumbling down around me. To be honest, I still have those flashes. But, they never last. And, if they do, there is one thing that will always get me through…

Gratitude, gratitude, gratitude – the antidote to negative thoughts, feelings and emotions. Over the course of the last two years, it is this appreciation for everything and everyone that has kept me optimistic and grounded.

Every morning, I look out the window. The sun is shining. There is life out there. It is beautiful and wonderful and I have the privilege of living to see it. I am so grateful that I get to wake up and enjoy this world. It really is a blessing.

Then, I think about the incredible medical teams who have treated and continue to treat me; of my wonderful family and friends who have offered up their unconditional love and support. I feel extremely lucky. Lucky to be in this hospital, lucky to have access to A grade medical facilities, lucky to be alive. I broke my leg and within 24 hours was on an operating table. We are so privileged in this country.

At the end of the day, I broke my leg. Do I wish it never happened? Of course! Can I change it? Absolutely not. Could it have been worse? Definitely. I'm not terminally ill. I'm not dying. I'm getting out of here alive. If that's not something to be grateful for, then I'm not sure what is.

If you are someone who struggles with negativity, I encourage you to practise gratitude. When you start thanking the universe for what you have, rather than what you have not, you will begin to see the positive in everything. Who wouldn't want that?

Write it out

When I was first admitted to hospital, I started tracking my thoughts and feelings. It was just a Word doc – nothing fancy – that I'd add to when I felt like rehashing my day or getting something off my chest. The journal helped me clear my mind – especially in those early days – giving me a place to expel my troubles by dumping them onto a page.

The more I journalled, the more I had to look back on. It was a wonderful thing, revisiting my recovery journey and seeing all the ways that I had changed. The highs and the lows, the setbacks and the support – it was all in there.

Journalling is a great habit to pick up, and can be beneficial in gaining perspective on problems, insight into behaviours and clarity around situations. Often, the second we feel an emotion, we act upon it. By taking a step back and committing our thoughts to paper first, we give your minds the space to decipher what is before us and analyse how we truly feel, so that we may respond appropriately.

* * *

It doesn't matter what you choose to do, but you should always take 45 minutes to one hour, five days a week, to work on yourself. It doesn't have to be journalling, or a vigorous gym session at 5:30 am (they are my salvations, my outlets). Instead, it could be walking, running, gardening, meditating – whatever you like. As long as you are prioritising yourself for that hour, it is up to you how you spend it. After all, it is your relationship with you that will ultimately get you through the dark times.

RELATIONSHIP WITH THE WORLD

As it stands today, I'm not sure what my future holds. I've just undergone yet another operation on my leg, hopefully to save it. But honestly, I don't really mind if it has to be amputated. I have made my peace with it. The only reason it wasn't done in the first place is because it is broken right up to the hip, which means I'd have to get everything, including my butt cheek, removed. I wouldn't be able to stand or sit down without leaning over. The docs want to do everything they can before they make that my reality.

Regardless of the outcome, I know it won't be much use anymore – I'll have minimal use of the leg. But, even if I am not the fit and able person I once was, I believe I will still have so much to offer – so much to give. I will pick up the pieces – even those that are broken and no good – and get ready to get back out there in whatever capacity I can. I'm ready to take on the world again.

For most of my life, I have offered up my time and services to various charities, organisations and fundraisers, and for the past 20 years, have volunteered with Country Fire Authority (CFA).

I remember Black Saturday – probably the worst job I have ever had to do. We were up there, dragging bodies out of the debris until one in the morning. No critical response team – just us, volunteers on the ground. And though that was probably the worst disaster I have had to deal with, I have witnessed countless other fatalities during my time with the CFA.

Now, you might be thinking *Rob, why on earth would you spend your spare time doing something like that?* Yes, it can be hard work, but is undeniably worth it. Why? Because giving back to my community fills me with purpose, drive and motivation. It makes me feel connected – like I am a part of something bigger. In fact, research has shown that altruistic endeavours promote a higher quality of life and can benefit "mental and physical health, life satisfaction, [and] social well-being."[1]

I don't think I'll be pointing the hose any time soon, but I believe there is some capacity in which I can offer my services. My support dog, Archie, comes in here quite often and I'd love to take him to the nursing homes or children's hospital, just to bring some cheer to the patients. We might even be adopting an old police horse at home. Perhaps I could offer rides to sick children – give them something fun to do to take their minds off things for a bit. Whatever it is, I want to give back by helping others deal with their health issues.

It is thoughts like these that keep me going on my worst days – that put a fire in my belly. There is a quote by Nick Vujicic that sums it up perfectly:

"You don't know what's around the corner until you go there."

I will never give up. I am planning for the best, but I am prepared for the worst.

Regardless of what happens, I'll make the most of it. Whether you are sick, healthy, or in recovery like me, I hope you do too.

ACKNOWLEDGEMENTS

I thank each and every one of these amazing authors who share their personal journey, their knowledge and their life lessons inside this book. They do this in such a selfless way; they help and teach others through their own journey and through knowledge gained from decades of experience, so that we the readers can learn, grow and shift our health and lives.

Even if just one of these stories can touch someone's life, to educate or awaken someone to make positive changes for their health, to become a better person, or to improve their health and life in a positive way, then we have achieved our goal.

We can change the world one story at a time. The honesty, vulnerability, courage and generosity that is shared by the YSHIFT authors in this extraordinary book of life stories and knowledge is truly inspirational. The authors allow us to learn from what they have either discovered themselves through hardship and growth, or studied to expert levels in their chosen field.

Thank you to my family and friends and my beautiful daughters Chloe and Monique for all their love and support. A special thank you to my amazing husband Michael, who has always believed in me and my dreams and supported me in more ways than one could ever image.

Sincere thanks to an amazing team of people who have helped this dream come to life: Natalie, Emma, Izzy, Jazmine, Dani, Matt, Chloe, Monique, Rhi, Mauraid, Suzan and all their supporting teams.

A special thank you to Don Tolman who shared his wisdom about health and nutrition, gained from decades of learning and teaching.

I am so grateful to all the readers and YSHIFT members, who all play a vital role in sharing forward these amazing stories and inspiring others to join the YSHIFT Movement, so that together we can change the world.

We are sharing more in the INTERACTIVE book.

See exclusive downloads, videos, audios and photos.

DOWNLOAD it for free at
deanpublishing.com/yshift/thriving

ENDNOTES

Fred Liberatore

1   Grucza, R., Lecroart, J.L., Hauser, J.J. et al. Dynamics of sweating in men and women during passive heating. *Europ. J. Appl. Physiol.* 54, 309–314 (1985). https://doi.org/10.1007/BF00426151 and KaciubaUscilko H, Grucza R. Gender differences in thermoregulation. *Current Opinion in Clinical Nutrition and Metabolic Care.* 2001 Nov;4(6):533-536. DOI: 10.1097/00075197-200111000-00012

2   Keele University. "Swearing Can Actually Increase Pain Tolerance." ScienceDaily. ScienceDaily, 13 July 2009. www.sciencedaily.com/releases/2009/07/090713085453.htm

3   Noel E. Brick, Megan J. McElhinney, Richard S. Metcalfe, 'The effects of facial expression and relaxation cues on movement economy, physiological, and perceptual responses during running.' *Psychology of Sport and Exercise*, Volume 34, 2018, https://doi.org/10.1016/j.psychsport.2017.09.009

Anna Von Zinner

1   World Health Organization (n.d.) *WHO Coronavirus (COVID-19) Dashboard*, WHO website, accessed 28 July 2021.

2   Black Dog Institute (2020) *Working from home: A checklist to support your mental health,* BDI website, accessed 28 July 2021.

3   Ibid.

4   Ashish Sharma, Vishal Madaan, Frederick D Petty (2006) 'Exercise for Mental Health', *Prim Care Companion J Clin Psychiatry*, 8(2): 106, doi: 10.4088/pcc.v08n0208a

5   *Australian online Macquarie dictionary*

6   Australian Government Department of Health (2020) *Additional 10 MBS mental health sessions during Covid-19* DoH website, accessed 28 July 2021.

7   Milad Mousazadeh, Biswaranian Paital, Zohreh Naghdali, Zohreh Mortezania, Marjan Hashemi, Elnaz Karamati Niaragh, Mohammad Aghababaei, Melika Ghorbankhani, Eric Lichtfouse, Mika Sallanpaa, Khalid S Hashim and Mohammad Mahdi Emamjomeh (2021) 'Positive environmental effects of the coronavirus 2020 episode: a review, *Environ Dev Sustain*, 1-23 doi: 10.1007/s10668-021-01240-3 [Epub ahead of print]

8   Ibid.

9   Ibid.

Julide Turker

1   Ibn Al-Qayyim (2018) *Provisions for the Hereafter*, El-Farouq.org.

2   Xavier Pi-Sunyer (2009) The Medical Risks of Obesity, *Postgrad Med* 121(6):21-33, doi: 10.3810/pgm.2009.11.2074

Marcus Pearce

1   Levy, B. R., Slade, M. D., Kunkel, S. R., & Kasl, S. V. (2002) 'Longevity increased by positive self-perceptions of aging', *Journal of Personality and Social Psychology*, 83(2), 261–270. https://doi.org/10.1037/0022-3514.83.2.261

2   Ibid.

3   Kenrick, Chris. (10 December 2018) 'Longtime aging expert, now 88, heeds his own advice', Palo Alto Online, accessed 8 June 2019. https://www.paloaltoonline.com/news/2018/12/09/longtime-aging-expert-now-88-heeds-his-own-advice

Myrna Manalili

1   Dr Myron Wentz (2002) Invisible Miracles - The Revolution in Cellular Nutrition, Medicis.

2   Global Environmental Facility Land Degradation, GEF website, accessed 5 May 2022.

3 Australian Government Department of Health (2021) *Physical Activity and Exercise Guidelines for all Australians, for adults 18 to 64 years*, DOH website, accessed 9 November 2021.

4 World Health Organisation (2021) Long working hours increasing deaths from heart disease and stroke: WHO, ILO, WHO website, accessed 5 May 2022.

5 Tommi Härkänen, Kari Kuulasmaa, Laura Sares-Jäske, Pekka Jousilahti, Markku Peltonen, Katja Borodulin, Paul Knekt, Seppo Koskinen (2020) 'Estimating expected life-years and risk factor associations with mortality in Finland: cohort study', *BMJ Open*, 10(3): e033741 doi: 10.1136/bmjopen-2019-033741.

6 Australian Institute of Health and Welfare (2021) Social isolation and loneliness, AIHW website, accessed 5 May 2022.

7 Liz Mineo (11 April 2017) 'Good genes are nice, but joy is better', The Harvard Gazette, accessed 5 May 2022.

8 United Nations, Department of Economic and Social Affairs, Population Division (2019) *World Population Prospects 2019: Highlights* [PDF 13.6MB], United Nations, accessed 9 November 2021.

9 Myra and Clive Hamilton (August 2006) Rich Boomer, Poor Boomer: Retirement prospects for the not-so-lucky generation [PDF 99KB], The Australia Institute, accessed 5 May 2022.

10 Seyul Kwak, Hairin Kim, Jeanyung Chey and Yoosik Youm (2018) 'Feeling How Old I Am: Subjective Age Is Associated With Estimated Brain Age', *Front Aging Neurosci*, 10:168, doi: 10.3389/fnagi.2018.00168.

11 Gerben J Westerhof, Martina Miche, Allyson F Brothers, Anne E Barrett, Manfred Diehl, Joann M Montepare, Hans-Werner Wahl and Susanne Wurm (2014) 'The Influence of Subjective Aging on Health and Longevity: A Meta-Analysis of Longitudinal Data', *Psychology and Aging*, 29(4):793-802, doi: 10.1037/a0038016.

12 Nutrition Australia (2013) *Nutrition and older adults* NA website, accessed 13 August 2021.

Tanya Leyson

1   Australian Bureau of Statistics (2018) Overweight and obesity, ABS website, accessed 21 May 2021.

2   OECD (2017) Obesity update, OECD website, accessed 21 May 2021.

3   Tarunpreet Saluja, Allan Davies, Chris Oldmeadow and Andrew J Boyle (2020) 'Impact of fast-food outlet density on incidence of myocardial infarction in the Hunter region', *Internal Medicine Journal*, 51(2): 243-248, doi: https://doi.org/10.1111/imj.14745

4   Mark Periera, Alex Kartashov, Cara B Ebbelingand Linda Van Horn (2005) 'Fast-Food Habits, Weight Gain, and Insulin Resistance (the CARDIA Study): 15-year prospective analysis', *The Lancet*, 365(9453): 36-42, doi:10.1016/S0140-6736(04)17663-0

5   Tarunpreet Saluja, Allan Davies, Chris Oldmeadow and Andrew J Boyle (2020) 'Impact of fast-food outlet density on incidence of myocardial infarction in the Hunter region', *Internal Medicine Journal*, 51(2): 243-248, doi: https://doi.org/10.1111/imj.14745

6   Gary is not his real name, of course!

Monique Sarup

1   *Macquarie Dictionary Online*, 2021, Macquarie Dictionary Publishers, an imprint of Pan Macmillan Australia Pty Ltd, www.macquariedictionary. com.au.

Robert Hall

1   Jerf W. K. Yeung, Zhuoni Zhang, and Tae Yeun Kim (2018) 'Volunteering and health benefits in general adults: cumulative effects and forms', *BMC Public Health*, 18(1):8, doi: 10.1186/s12889-017-4561-8.

Lightning Source UK Ltd.
Milton Keynes UK
UKHW010653160223
417122UK00019B/1919